THE TAMAR VALLEY

THE INDUSTRIAL ARCHAEOLOGY
OF THE BRITISH ISLES

Series Editor: E. R. R. GREEN

Derbyshire, by Frank Nixon
The East Midlands, by David M. Smith
Galloway, by Ian Donnachie
Hertfordshire, by W. Branch Johnson
The Lake Counties, by J. D. Marshall and M. Davies-Shiel
Lancashire, by Owen Ashmore
Scotland, by John Putt
Southern England (second edition, revised), by Kenneth Hudson

ASSOCIATED VOLUMES

The Bristol Region, by R. A. Buchanan and Neil Cossons
Dartmoor, by Helen Harris
Gloucestershire Woollen Mills, by Jennifer Tann
Stone Blocks and Iron Rails, by Bertram Baxter
The Tamar Valley (second impression, revised), by Frank Booker
Techniques of Industrial Archaeology, by J. P. M. Pannell

OTHER INDUSTRIAL HISTORY

The British Iron and Steel Industry, by W. K. V. Gale
The Early Factory Masters, by Stanley D. Chapman
The Engineering Industry of the North of Ireland, by W. E. Coe
The History of Water Power in Ulster, by H. D. Gribbon

All these books are in uniform format

The Industrial Archaeology of

THE TAMAR VALLEY

FRANK BOOKER

DAVID & CHARLES: NEWTON ABBOT

ISBN 0 7153 5172 9

First published 1967
Second impression, revised, 1971

Set in Imprint, 11 pt 2 pt leaded
and printed in Great Britain
by Latimer Trend & Co Ltd Plymouth
for David & Charles (Publishers) Limited
South Devon House   Newton Abbot   Devon

Contents

5

List of Illustrations

In memory of P——

PART ONE

Author's Note

FOR this impression I have made a few amendments to the text in the light of further information. These chiefly refer to Morwellham, to the engines working Pearson's quarry and to the incline plane on the Mill Hill 'cut'. Now that Tavistock is no longer served by a railway the chapter on the LSWR has been revised. Opportunity has also been taken to correct some mis-spellings.

CHAPTER ONE

The Strange Dichotomy

TWISTING and turning upon itself in great loops and bends, the river Tamar between Gunnislake and Plymouth flows through a hilly and tumbled valley rich in surprises. Half in Cornwall, half in Devon, its unusual and varied scenery is among the least known in the country and it hides relics of an industrial past hardly known outside Devon and Cornwall.

The Tamar Valley today is devoted to agriculture, but in the 1850s and 60s it rivalled West Cornwall in importance as a source of copper. For nearly thirty years after that it was the centre of arsenic production in the British Isles, and it had long been recognized as an important area of lead and silver mining. At a time when ships were changing from sail to steam, furnace-linings for marine boilers were made from the growan clay of its granite hills; bricks from the same clay found a ready export as far afield as Russia.

All these industries—one employed over a thousand people while others were little more than family enterprises—grew up in an isolated countryside where people lived in close contact with their surroundings. Its compact and close-knit character is well illustrated by looking at Calstock in the days when all the mineral produce of East Cornwall was shipped through its quays down the Tamar to the sea. The rise and decline of this river port illustrates the story of the Tamar Valley.

Today Calstock has one of the highest unemployment rates in Devon and Cornwall; one quarry works where once there were ten. But between the 1860s and 80s a man living there could have been housed, clothed and shod with bricks, serge[1] and leather produced within a mile of its quays. Paint coloured by ochre produced from

13

one of half a dozen mines in the area could have been used to
decorate his house. Beer brewed locally would have slaked his thirst
and a mill by the river's edge made brown paper to wrap his pur-
chases. A ship-owner or merchant, he could have sailed on the
coastal trade to Portugal in a schooner built and largely fitted out by
the quayside, and as a farmer he was able to use fertilizer and lime
ground and burnt in the parish, and as likely as not hand-tools
forged in a local hammer mill.

Industry and agriculture formed close and subtle connections
with each other to become part of an economic complex that today
is completely shattered. Brickmaking and quarrying have now become concentrated near larger centres of population where transport
is more convenient. No worthwhile mining has taken place in the
district since 1900, and by the first world war nearly a quarter of its
working population had emigrated. The Tamar, which had been a
highway for all the trade and supplies of the district, became—and
has remained—a deserted river, killed by the railway and improvements in road transport.

This picture of a once-important industrial area overtaken by
decline and change has parallels in many other areas, but two factors
set the Tamar Valley apart from other districts developed by Victorian enterprise and industrial expansion, and they affect its
economy and character today. The first is a market-garden tradition
probably older than its industry. The Valley had long supplied
Plymouth and the Navy with vegetables and fruit, and at the height
of its industrial development, when mining, smelting and arsenic
refining were helping to fill the river valley with dense fogs,* horticulture was rapidly expanded far beyond the need and resources of
the immediate neighbourhood to supply markets in London, the
north of England and Scotland. Strangers to the area were often

---

* Fogs in the Tamar Valley, aggravated by industrial smoke from works along the
river bank, are unknown today, but in the nineteenth century they were a common
and serious hazard to shipping. Leases often specified that chimneys of arsenic
refineries should be of sufficient height to discharge above the fog belt.

astonished to see the vegetation on the upper slopes of the valleys blighted by the fumes of arsenic refineries, while lower down early strawberries and cherries grew in profusion, among them the famous black mazzards which the Victorians pickled in brandy to make a liqueur delicacy.

A second and equally incongruous factor was its fame as a beauty spot. The Tamar Valley in the nineteenth century was as celebrated for its scenery as its mines. J. M. W. Turner sought it out to paint the river views. Paddle steamers brought thousands of people to Calstock and Weir Head, not to see the mines or gape at the 'hydraulic machinery' which wheezed on the river bank, but to wander and picnic among some of the most romantic scenery in the south of England. This scenery remained largely unspoilt by mining works through the strict exercise of an almost feudal right of ownership, which has had a permanent effect on the appearance and development of the valley and has subtly affected its character.

For until 1959 much of the Devon bank of the Tamar from Horsebridge to Gawton had known only two owners in a thousand years—the Abbots of the great Benedictine Abbey of Tavistock and the Dukes of Bedford to whom the abbey's lands were given after the Dissolution.* The monks, who had little interest in the tin streaming and mining activities around them, built up instead a well-organized and healthy pastoral economy. This outlook and policy was carried on and even extended by the new owners. Successive Dukes of Bedford allowed no building or mineral prospecting without compensation clauses and dues so onerous that, as intended, they hindered rather than aided development. It needed hardihood and endless persistence to seek a mine lease from the Duke of Bedford, for the dues in some cases amounted to 100 per

---

* It was one of the biggest land grants—one-sixth of all the monastic lands of Devon—in English history and from a king not noted for his generosity. The fact that it was given to a family entirely unconnected with the area has given rise to the suspicion that the king wanted someone who would keep an eye on his uncertain western subjects. (See *Devon Monastic Lands*, page 21.)

cent over the agricultural value of the land. The royalties received from Devon Great Consols mine—and they far exceeded those from any other mineral working in Devon—were never regarded by the

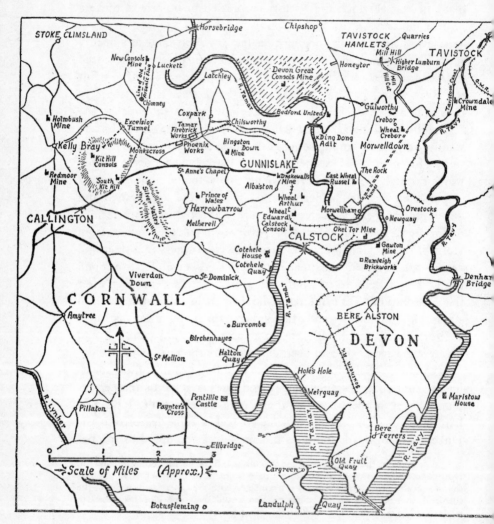

The Tamar Valley

seventh and eighth dukes as sufficient compensation for the loss of 140 acres of pheasant coverts.

Similarly below the Bedford lands the Mount Edgcumbe family has held a discriminating tenure for over 500 years of almost all the Bere Alston peninsula and the woodlands of Cotehele on the Cornish bank. In this way substantial stretches of countryside containing some of the finest scenery in the valley and some of its richest mineral ground have remained for centuries in the hands of two great landowning families. Only at Calstock has this continuity been broken[2]. Here, at the beginning of the nineteenth century, the old Norman manor lands fell into the hands of mining prospectors who have left scars that still remain unhealed. Gunnislake, a typical nineteenth-century mining settlement, sprawls in squalid and uncontrolled confusion over a noble granite hillside. The Devon bank only escaped similar treatment at the beginning of the nineteenth century through the jealous land-preserving policy of the sixth Duke of Bedford. Such inhibition of development often caused hardship.

Few areas owe more to their geographical and geological features than the Tamar Valley. Drawn on the map, the district resembles a triangle tilted towards the west and stretching from Horsebridge north of Gunnislake to the tip of the Bere Alston peninsula in the south. Here the Tavy, bringing with it the waters of Dartmoor, forms the valley's eastern boundary, while on the Cornish side the A 388 road from Callington to Saltash limits its western extent. In the north, Callington and Tavistock, 10 miles apart, form its north-western and north-eastern outposts. Between these two centres runs a ridge of high ground, at its highest point at Kit Hill over 1,000 ft above sea level, developed in granite on the Cornish side, but appearing as slates on the Devon bank. This ridge has played an important part in the industrial development of the district for it is the source of its mineral wealth and of the hard short-grained granite that has gone into Singapore Dockyard and helped to keep the Thames in bounds along its embankment. The ridge is also a

B

shield. It keeps out the north winds, and this combined with the influence of the sea helps to give the Valley a climate almost perfect for fruit growing. Day and night temperatures probably vary less than anywhere else in England. There is no abrupt change of seasons and cattle can be kept in the fields all the year round. A prevailing westerly wind straight off the sea gives a moderately high rainfall and this on the sun-catching south- and east-facing valleys ripens fruit a profitable fortnight earlier than elsewhere in the country.

South from this dominating northern ridge Devonian slates and shales with carboniferous inliers slope away to the Tamar's estuary forming first, near Calstock and Bere Alston, a countryside of steep-sided valleys with an almost rooflike pitch for which a special pattern and method of ploughing has had to be evolved. Closer to Plymouth and Saltash the steep valleys give way to rolling and park-like down-land falling to reedy river margins rich in bird life. It is an area of wide vistas, dramatic views and plunging waterfalls. The characteristic settlements reflect the strange dichotomy of the valley. There are the little cherry and strawberry villages of Botus Fleming, St Mellion, Bere Ferrers and St Dominic, whose populations can be counted in hundreds on the fingers of one hand. On the bleaker upland slopes are the old mining centres of Calstock and Callington and the bare white and grey villages of Latchley, Luckett, Stoke Climsland and Kelly Bray—villages surrounded by the ruined engine-houses of the mines which called them into being, or backed by gaping holes in the ground from where stone has been quarried.

The Tamar itself, a tidal river for the 19 miles of its course below Gunnislake to its estuary at Plymouth, binds together and imparts a single character to an area it divides politically as the boundary between Devon and Cornwall. In a countryside whose steep hills and valleys make it the despair of road builders it is the natural highway, and until the coming of the railway it controlled and vitally influenced local development. Until 1962 there was no road bridge across it below Gunnislake, and the quays and ferry points which grew up along its banks were the chief means of communication between its two shores. Until 1908 the river was also the easiest means of reaching Bere Alston, Calstock and Callington and the mining and quarrying villages above Gunnislake. Vessels of 300 tons could navigate it to the now forgotten and decaying port of Morwellham, and 50-ton barges with coal, sand and manure could thread their way to Gunnislake.

The Tamar was also the principal source of power in the valley. The background to the industrial development of the Tamar Valley is the gurgle of water in a leat and the thud and clank of water-wheels. The cost of transporting coal from South Wales around Land's End and up the long south Cornish coastline was so high that the success or failure of a mine in the area was largely dependent on the availability of a good water supply, and the employment of water as a means of power reached a level of ingenuity unsurpassed elsewhere in the country. Leats to carry it were contoured for miles along hillsides and tunnelled through rocks. Water-wheels were used underground as well as on the surface[3]. The huge Devon Great Consols mine had at one time thirty-three wheels and in its earliest and most prosperous years obtained the bulk of its power for as little as £5 a week from water lifted from the Tamar by water-wheels pumping 500 gallons a minute. Wheal Friendship mine, near Tavistock, used water from the Tavy to turn wheels which did all the hauling, crushing and pumping on the mine, a steam engine being kept in reserve only for drought. Water-wheels drained and ventilated the Tavistock Canal tunnel during its construction, and supplied the power for incline planes and corn and paper mills. The biggest of them developed up to 140 horse power, their ceaseless turning interrupted only by a dry spell or severe frost, when, so much was their rhythmic pounding a part of the everyday background, people were said to be unable to sleep.

The mineral field of the Tamar Valley has been especially rich in

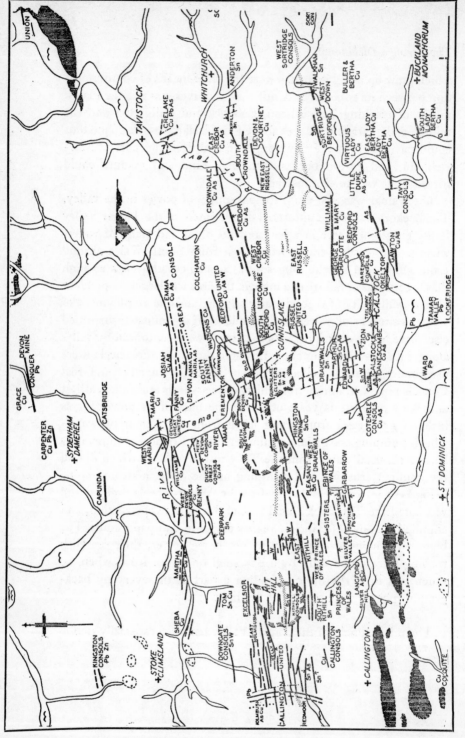

The pattern of the lodes—the short lines trending east–west mark the tin and copper lodes. Those north–south are lead

copper and arsenic, only slightly less so in tin, while silver, lead, wolfram, and manganese have all been mined in quantity.* The source of this mineral field as mentioned earlier is the granite intrusion pushed up through older slates between Kit Hill and Gunnislake. This granite disappears abruptly on the surface almost at the river's edge at Gunnislake to crop up again in the Dartmoor tors beyond Tavistock[4]. The tin and copper lodes lie closest to the granite and run east-north-east, but the lead and silver veins developed farther away from it strike boldly as cross-courses in a north-south direction. Near Plymouth a silver-lead lode was worked on what is now a large housing estate although its source was probably the Plympton granite rather than Gunnislake.†

How richly mineralized the area is becomes strikingly apparent on a geological map. The tin and copper veins are seen densely bunched through a belt 4 miles wide and 12 miles long between Tavistock and Callington, while the lead lodes trend in sharp contrast in thick solid lines due south. That almost all of them were deposited at comparatively shallow depths explains their often chance discovery and the short working life of many of the mines. Copper has been found only 5 ft from the surface, and some of the richest ore shoots in Devon Great Consols mine were above the natural level of drainage. The early discovery of the Bere Alston mines was probably because the lodes almost outcropped on the ridge. Any major excavation is likely to reveal a mineral lode; Wheal Crebor near Tavistock was discovered in the digging of the Tavistock Canal tunnel, and nearly eighty years later railway navvies disturbed a

* The heavy mineralization of the area has been linked with a high cancer incidence. Collections for cancer charities around Albaston average between £1,000 and £800 a year.

† This was Wheal Whitleigh (or Wheal Guinness or Gennys), which produced 1,436 oz of silver and 36 tons of lead before it ceased working about 1856. Copper has also been found in Plymouth, commemorated today in the name of 'Copper Place' and (in 1850) when the foundations for the new prison (now the Plymouth police headquarters) were being excavated. The lode crosses the old Tavistock turnpike road at North Hill (P & DWJ, 8 August 1850).

lode while excavating the nearby Shilla Mill tunnel of the old
London & South Western Railway. When the river is low a
copper lode can be seen in the bed of the Tamar below Horsebridge.

It was this mineral wealth which led mining to dominate the
industrial development of the Tamar Valley, although the lime
trade, agriculture and quarrying are much older industries. The
first reliable record of mining dates from the thirteenth century,
when the silver recovered from the shallow workings near Bere
Alston enriched the treasury of Edward I. The early workings in
that and the succeeding century on what was then a remote peninsula probably saw the beginnings of shaft mining in England as well
as the first use of adits for draining mines.

By comparison copper mining was late in starting and was confined with unimportant exceptions to the nineteenth century and
the northern half of the Valley. It began in earnest in the Napoleonic
wars, when in the first ten years of the century over 30,000 tons of
copper worth £330,000 were mined between Mary Tavy and the
Devon bank of the Tamar,* and reached its most prosperous years
between 1844 and 1870. In those years, under the stimulus of the
discovery of Devon Great Consols mine at Blanchdown, near
Tavistock, and the reopening of a number of previously abandoned
workings, the Tamar Valley became the richest copper-producing
centre in England and some of the highest-grade ore ever to be
treated in this country went down the Tamar to the smelting works
of South Wales. When by 1856 the output of copper ore from
Cornwall and the Tamar Valley had reached a maximum of 209,000
tons, over 29,000 tons had come from Devon Great Consols mine.
Eight years later out of a total production of 48,977 tons from
twenty copper mines in Devon, 26,696 tons were contributed from
Devon Great Consols; furthermore it was worth nearly three-
quarters as much as all the ore from the other nineteen Devon

* Risdon's *Survey of Devonshire*, 1811.

mines. These 'copper' years filled the Valley with miners and the Tamar with shipping. It became the centre of the 'copper kingdom'. Mining activity circulated £10,000 a month in Tavistock[5], while the shipment of ores was the principal business of all the river quays between Morwellham and the Bere Alston peninsula.

Little less remarkable was the period that saw arsenic production topple the supremacy of copper and prolong the life of a number of mines for almost thirty years. The arsenic deposits in the Tamar Valley were among the richest and most extensive in England, and the arsenic-refining plant on Devon Great Consols, one of over half a dozen in the neighbourhood, was successively enlarged until it covered 8 acres—the largest in England and producing half the world's arsenic. Visitors in the 1880s used to be told—and it was probably true—that enough was stored there to poison the world's population.

At the height of the mining boom in the Tamar Valley over 100 mines large and small were at work, served by a host of ancillary trades employing rope makers, blacksmiths, wheelwrights, boilermakers and foundrymen. Good boilermakers were sufficiently scarce to obtain over £1 a week, whereas the average wage of a skilled miner was between 13s and 15s. The Bedford foundry at Tavistock —one of three in the town—built mine pumping engines and also what were probably the first iron canal boats ever to be used in this country. Mining enterprise improved communications in the area, first with the Tavistock Canal and later with the narrow-gauge East Cornwall Mineral Railway. Devon Great Consols built and maintained the first standard-gauge railway in the Valley, solely to carry its ores more quickly and cheaply to Morwellham. The effect of mining on the population of the district is vividly shown in the nineteenth-century census returns.

In Tavistock in 1861, 2,193 people were employed in mining, only 278 less than in agriculture, traditionally the main source of employment in the area, while the declining cloth industry em-

ployed only 99. Manganese mining, active along the north-eastern
perimeter of the Valley between Brentor and Gunnislake, its produce shipped through Morwellham, brought striking increases in
the populations of Lifton, Coryton, Stowford and Lewtrenchard.
These doubled in the fifty years between 1801 and 1851, reaching
a figure twice as large as today's.

	1801	*1831*	*1841*	*1851*	*1861*
Bere Alston	1,110	1,876	2,142	3,401	2,876*
Tavistock	3,420	5,602	6,272	8,147	8,965
Calstock†	1,105	2,388	2,553	4,356	7,090
Callington	819	1,388	1,685	2,138	2,173

But this apparent prosperity was precariously based. Well over
half the capital in mining came from outside investors and specu-
lators interested only in dividends. As the first signs of the impend-
ing collapse in copper mining appeared in the 1860s[6], the capital
which held many mines together vanished overnight, and hundreds
of men, women and children found themselves without work in an
area which had little large-scale alternative employment to offer
them. Between 1861 and 1901 the population of Tavistock declined
by over 3,000, of Calstock by 1,000 and of Callington by nearly 500.
Men emigrated in such numbers that the district nearly bled to
death and two shipping agents were kept fully employed in Gunnislake; the ill-fated *Titanic* carried among its steerage passengers a
quota of emigrating Tamar Valley miners. The despatch of parcels
and letters to Canada, the United States of America, South Africa
and Australia for the descendants of those who emigrated during
those times accounts today for a large proportion of the business of
Gunnislake's small post office.

What is left today of this busy industrial world which filled the

---

* The decrease here is largely attributable to the disaster to the South Tamar
mine, flooded when the Tamar broke into its workings in 1856.
   † Including Gunnislake.

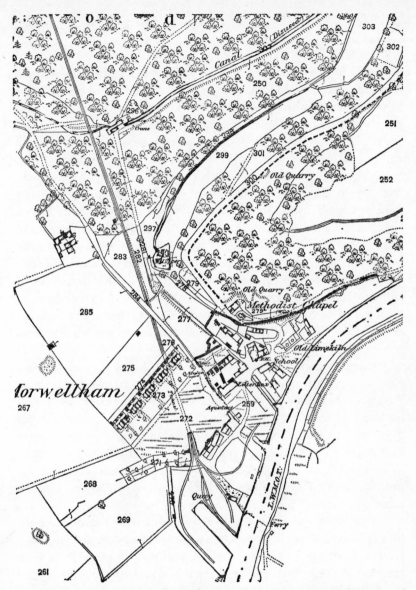

Morwellham as shown in the 1880 ordnance survey. The course of
the incline connecting with the Tavistock canal is plainly shown.
The tramway on the left is the Devon Great Consols incline

villages with people and crowded the river quays with shipping? Socially, mining turned the Tamar Valley into a slum. Five or more families often crowded together in houses where eight people slept in one room. In the 'hard' times of 1866 and 67 many of the poor were without underclothes, sleeping on straw and 'eating coarse dry bread'. Water supplies depended on mine leats or on wells adjacent to cesspits. Cholera was almost endemic and infant mortality from so-called 'malignant fevers' was twice that of adjacent districts. On one day in August 1864 the rector of Calstock, himself heavily bereaved, took seven funerals and had to prohibit any more bodies being taken into the church. Tavistock was so overcrowded and living conditions so revolting that the outraged Portreeve personally petitioned the Duke of Bedford to provide land for more houses[7]; one result of this appeal can be seen today in the neat rows of cottages at West Bridge, Fitzford, Gulworthy and other places in and around Tavistock. Built mainly in 1850–60, they are remarkable examples of an experiment in industrial housing design well in advance of its time.

A more substantial legacy is the Tavistock Canal, completed in 1817 and apart from its incline plane down to Morwellham docks virtually intact. The group of nineteenth-century warehouse buildings and slate-fronted cottages around the remains of the canal wharf at Tavistock has irresistible period charm. The town centre of Tavistock, laid out and rebuilt by the seventh Duke of Bedford in the middle of the last century, owes its pleasant and spacious proportions to the royalties derived from Devon Great Consols mine.

For the rest one must tramp over damp river meadows, push through thickets or climb over the slopes of Morwell and Hingston Down. A strange, little-known but exciting countryside is then revealed, poignantly evocative of a vanished industrial age and full of the memorials of what once made it alive.

CHAPTER TWO

The Tamar Quays and Ferries

THE Tamar is the strongest natural boundary in England. For the greater part of its length since the tenth century it has divided Devon and Cornwall and has always been a difficult obstacle to cross. There was no bridge over it for 30 miles above Plymouth until Polson bridge was built in the thirteenth century to carry into Cornwall the great northern highway from Exeter. Below Gunnislake, until Brunel built his railway bridge in 1859 the river had to be crossed by ferries. The toll bridge between Plymouth and Saltash opened in 1961 is a modern luxury[1].

Almost all the quays along the Tamar between Gunnislake and Plymouth began as ferry crossings. The history of some of them, such as the once-important 'passages' at what are now Halton Quay (the gateway to East Cornwall) and Calstock, reach back beyond Saxon times. In a countryside where deep valleys and streams impeded overland movement the ferry crossings became the obvious receipt and despatch points for goods carried up and down the river. Weir Quay near Bere Alston and Martinstow (Maristow) on the Tavy not only had a ferryman but were quays serving the silver mines in the thirteenth century, while Cargreen, lower down on the Cornish shore, once sent ships to sea, mainly on a coastwise trade.

MORWELLHAM

Few of these quays and crossings have a more crowded history than Morwellham, 1½ miles below Gunnislake where the Tamar mingles with tidal water. One hundred years ago, borne on the

27

wings of Victorian mining enterprise, it was the busiest inland river port in Devon and Cornwall. Sailors from the Baltic knew it as well as ships' captains from the New World; copper from its quays went to the East Indies.

Today Morwellham is a 'ghost village', lost amid a desolation of weed and ooze, but still remarkable for its unexpected situation, encountered suddenly at the foot of a steep slope. The silent road down to it is flanked by a high bank from which ferns sprout and water continually drains. At the bottom the tiny port lies like a small saucer backed by sharply rising tree-clad ground. The Tamar here is muddy and insignificant, and the sight of ships' masts gradually appearing above the reeds astonished travellers and crews approaching for the first time. Vessels of up to 300 tons could reach Morwellham; only four miles from Tavistock and two hours away by river from Plymouth, it was serving as a port to Tavistock when the town was granted a weekly market in 1105, and by 1238 its harbour dues were rewarding to the manor of Morwell in whose lands it lay. Through Morwellham came pipes of cider for Tavistock Abbey from Plympton, dried fish (particularly mackerel, herring and hake), and above all sea-sand, dredged from the estuary 19 miles downstream and taken inland by pack horses for liming the fields.

When in the twelfth century Dartmoor was the richest source of tin in Europe, Morwellham was well placed to handle the export of a lot of the coigned blocks of tin. In fact Tavistock, where in 1305 five coinages* were held, was the only stannary town out of three in Devon to have a port on a navigable river. The last tin coinage to be held in Devon took place at Morwellham in 1838 when 756 blocks weighing about 126 tons were stamped with the arms of the Duchy of Cornwall. The coinage duties on tin were abolished in that year.

---

* The 'coign' was the piece chiselled off a block of tin for assaying its quality before sale. 'Coinage' or stannary towns were simply the towns appointed for this to be done and had nothing to do with the making or coining of money.

Morwellham's use and importance increased rapidly after the completion of the Tavistock Canal in 1817 (see Chapter Six), which halved the cost and time of carriage to and from Tavistock. At this time as well as the lead and copper ores from Wheal Betsy and Wheal Friendship (whose new-found prosperity had benefited the whole district), all the copper output—nearly 23,000 tons between 1805 and 1819—from the newly discovered Wheal Crebor mine in the Tavistock Canal tunnel passed through the port which imported coal, timber, linseed, salt, lime and manure. The copper exports were closely rivalled in importance by increasing shipments of manganese, from mines discovered to the north of Tavistock at the beginning of the century and which were among the principal source of manganese in the United Kingdom at a time when it was largely used in glass manufacture. The Tavistock manganese mines lay above the route of the canal, the ore being brought to Morwellham in wagons. In this way 1,335 tons were shipped through to Plymouth in 1819 and 2,212 tons in 1821. Later manganese began to be used increasingly in the manufacture of steel and the production of chlorine gas for bleaching cotton, and the Tavistock mines for a while had a near-monopoly of the domestic market. The ore was ground for the chemical industries in a water-mill on the quay, packed in 4 cwt casks and exported from a special manganese dock to keep it apart from the arsenic ores[2].

Morwellham when the Tavistock Canal was completed had two large quays to take ships of 200 tons, a timber yard, a blacksmith's shop and a copper-ore yard where the present hydro-electric station now stands. The quays were edged with water meadows and the houses with walled gardens full of fruit and flowers—'a peaceful yet busy spot' with 'shouting sailors, hammering workmen and a train of wagons ascending and descending the incline'. This rustic scene of industry and peace was sharply jolted in November 1844 by the discovery at Blanchdown, 5 miles from Tavistock, of the rich copper deposits which became Devon Great Consols mine (see Chapter

Eight). Morwellham almost overnight became virtually part of the mine whose piles of glistening ore overflowed its quays on to those of adjoining Newquay and Gawton.

There were never less than 4,000 tons of ore on the quay floors, where it was sampled at the rate of 2,000 tons a month. The limited quay space threatened to restrict the production of the mine, until in 1859 a new dock 290 ft long, 60 ft wide and 16 ft deep, capable of taking six vessels of 300 tons, was opened. The old-world houses with their gardens were swept away to make room for more paved ore floors and by the end of the century nearly 750,000 tons of copper ore and 72,000 tons of arsenic, worth in all about £3,500,000, had been shipped through the quays of Morwellham from Devon Great Consols mine.

Among the imports during this time were 2,500 loads of timber a year from Baltic, Canadian and Pacific forests and 200 tons of coal a month, along with iron, ropes and 'sundries' for the mine foundry. There was also a steady 15,000 to 16,000 tons a year of miscellaneous cargo arising from the independent trade carried over the Tavistock Canal. The Duke of Bedford collected 4d on every ton of copper and 2d on timber and iron. In 1857 the dues from Morwellham were £899.

Morwellham in the middle years of the nineteenth century was by far the most interesting place on the river. Two incline planes were working within 100 yards of each other—one serving the Tavistock Canal and the other linking the docks with the railway built for Devon Great Consols mine. Trucks coming down this rumbled through a tunnel, clattering out on to staging erected over the ore quays. Barrels for arsenic and manganese were made in a cooper's shed by the quay and hooped in an adjoining blacksmith's shop. All work was at piece rates: the men who wheeled the ore in barrows from the trucks were paid $2\frac{1}{2}$d a ton; those who unloaded ships received $1\frac{1}{2}$d; for extra effort a free pint of beer or cider was granted. It took two days to unload a 400-ton vessel; there were no mecha-

nical aids on the quays. Accidents were common; one man was cut
in half by the tautening cable wire as he took a short cut across
Devon Great Consols incline; another was crushed to death when
some sheerlegs upholding the staging on the quay collapsed. Sailors
were always in the port. Each month assayers and buyers from the
South Wales smelting works gathered to sample, weigh and test the
ores in a laboratory by the quayside before they were shipped for
ticketing at Truro. Along with ships' captains they were put up in
the roomy Ship Inn, busy enough to provide appointments 'equal
to those to be found in a hotel in a small town'.

By the middle of the century the population had trebled, and the
Duke of Bedford had been forced to put up twenty cottages adjoining the timber quay. There was a village shop, a school with two
teachers for over fifty children, two limekilns constantly at work and
a corn mill worked by a 25 ft water-wheel which was later to provide
power for the manganese mill already mentioned. Dissenters had
two chapels on the spot; the Anglicans, less lucky, had to walk $1\frac{1}{2}$
miles to the Gulworthy church erected by the Duke of Bedford. In
1876 there was even a plan to link the port with the East Cornwall
Mineral Railway (see Chapter Nine) by a viaduct across the river at
Gawton, but a slump in the mining industry killed the project[3].

Few river ports in the West of England have handled so much
mineral wealth or known such busy scenes; few have died so swiftly.
The seeds of Morwellham's doom were carried by the railway which
had reached Tavistock from Plymouth in 1859. Ten years later it
had been extended to Launceston and took so much of the trade of
the Tavistock Canal that by 1873 that waterway had been abandoned
as a navigation.* By 1888 the canal incline down to Morwellham had
been torn up, the trucks were lying smashed and winding gear
left in ruins by the hillside. The port then became entirely linked to
the fortunes of Devon Great Consols mine, and by the end of the

---

* In 1869 lime from Billacombe quarry, Plymstock, was being burnt and taken
to Launceston by rail.

1880s this too was beyond hope. A visitor to Morwellham in 1896 found its quays deserted[4]. In 1901 Devon Great Consols mine ceased production, but its port predeceased it, after nearly 1,000 years of active life.

Today life is returning to Morwellham. Its hydro-electric station and the canal feeding it may face an uncertain future, but a new chapter in its story is opening up with the establishment of a field study centre sponsored by the Dartington Amenity Research Trust. Along with a hostel, there will be a museum to reflect the industrial and agricultural life of the area, and under a warden's guidance the quays are being cleared of undergrowth to give a clearer idea of their extent. This is revealing more sharply an older dock in line with the canal incline and showing more clearly the pattern of tiling on the quays as well as revealing some of the post holes for the overhead staging of the mine railway. Always prominent have been the evocative granite mooring blocks of the big mine dock and clearance may reveal more. The slate-fronted house with its bow window looking on to the quays once accommodated the harbour master and has been a shop. Marks on its side show how high the Tamar can rise in time of flood. Next to it the stucco-fronted dwelling house, now much reduced in size, was the Ship Inn celebrated for its roast beef and 'stout October' ale. Adjoining it at the back is an old kiln (there are finer and bigger ones on the river bank) which has been used as a baker's oven. In the gap between these buildings ran the Tavistock Canal incline. There are remains of slate sleepers here with holes drilled for the rail chair spikes. A waterwheel, once used for pumping water, is still *in situ* near here.

The massive abandoned grindstone comes from the now de-molished manganese mill which had a waterwheel fed by a launder of which a pier and the wheel pit still remain. Close by is the arsenic store shed with a little dock at the back for loading. In front of the cottages built by the Duke of Bedford lies the timber yard once piled high with timber from Baltic and Canadian forests. Under it

Morwellham, circa 1870. Piles of ore awaiting shipment are on the quays. The path of the two inclines can be seen in the background

The Morwellham scene today. The paving tiles in the foreground once covered the quays. The main dock excavated in 1858–9 was immediately on the right of the picture

Slate tramway sleepers leading from the old Tavistock canal incline at Morwellham

Old ore chute, one of a number to be seen in the retaining wall of the old copper quay at Morwellham

ran the tunnel from Devon Great Consols incline in line with the
gap between the first pair of cottages.

Finally on the old copper quay can still be seen the chutes
through which mineral ores brought by road by the heavy ore
wagons were once tipped to the quay below.

CALSTOCK

The counterpart to Morwellham on the Cornish bank of the
Tamar is Calstock, 3 miles farther downstream. With its huddle of
houses—one terrace looking down on the roof of another—and its
steep streets rushing to the river's edge, Calstock looks more like a
Cornish seaport than a river-quay town, but it has grown up around
one of the oldest crossings of the Tamar. In the nineteenth century
it had over a quarter of a mile of quays, was the centre of a registered
shipping company and had a tug permanently stationed off the
quays to manœuvre barges and pull big timber loads.

Calstock was a river quay in Saxon times and surnames suggest
a Breton origin for some of its inhabitants[5]. But it had no market
charter and thus lacked an influential merchant population. This, in
the Middle Ages, meant that it had no ships of its own to send to
sea. Instead, its barges carried on an entrepôt trade up and down
the river. In 1462–63 barges from Calstock were carrying sand, lime
and granite moorstone for the repair of Trematon Mill, Saltash, the
stone being split on the quayside with wedges and dressed with
hammers, picks and chisels. The carriage of lime for mortar at this
time also suggests an early barge traffic in limestone from Plymouth.

Mining has been part of Calstock's history for several centuries
and until the coinage dues were abolished in 1838 it often served as
a coinage town. Tin was recovered at Kit Hill and at Drakewalls
long before the Napoleonic wars stimulated the search for minerals,
but the emergence of Calstock as a nineteenth-century mining centre

c

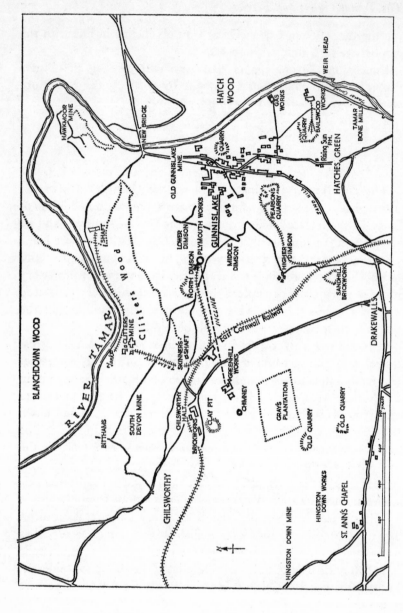

Industrial development around Gunnislake

begins with the discovery in the 1770s of the rich copper deposits
running eastwards under the river to the Devon bank, worked at the
Gunnislake Old Mine. By 1800 this mine had brought a fortune to
the Williams family of Scorrier, and it was at its most profitable in
the first fifteen years of the century. Gunnislake grew up around its
busy engine-house. John Williams put up cottages for his workmen
each with a garden large enough for a pig. He also developed
quarries in the area, seeking contracts for the stone in Devonport
and Plymouth. The family grip on the neighbourhood became so
complete that between 1816 and 1821 the alternative name for
Gunnislake was Williams Town[6]. On the outskirts of Callington,
Kelly Bray similarly grew up as a mining settlement around the
Holmbush mine whose spoil-heaps can be seen today along the
Stoke Climsland road.

Like Tavistock, Calstock saw its most active and prosperous
mining years after 1840 when prospecting was feverishly pursued
under the stimulus of the discovery of Devon Great Consols mine.
In 1865 at least seventeen mines were working within 5 miles of
Calstock, producing not only copper and arsenic but also quantities
of tin, silver and lead. Okel Tor mine on the river bank just above
the town built its own quays to ship its ore. The annual outputs
from these mines were pigmy in comparison with that from Devon
Great Consols mine, but collectively they added up to substantial
totals. All of it was weighed and sampled on Calstock quay, which
after 1859 was served by a steam-operated incline, saving the wagons
the long and often dangerous journey through the steep main street
of the town.

According to the *Cornwall and Devon Mining Directory* published
in 1862 by Banfield Brothers of Hayle, 2,169 people were engaged
in mining in the area between Callington and Calstock. The district
also supplied a large part of the labour force employed at Devon
Great Consols, and in 1870 the slump in mining due to the depression in the metal market inflicted on Calstock all the hardship

of a depressed area. Only seven mines were left in 1878, and by 1883 only two. Copper production had by then virtually ceased in the area, and the principal mining activity for the rest of the century was arsenic refining.

But unlike Morwellham, Calstock had other resources. It had a hinterland providing a greater variety of employment and trade than any other centre in the Tamar Valley. A guide book published in 1881 could refer to the area's 'immense resources for industry, manufacture and trade' and go on to list more than a dozen enterprises of which but one exists today[7]. Only Plymouth could offer a wider industrial network for at Calstock at this time were papermills, brick and tile works, a brewery, a tannery, shipbuilding yards and quarries. Some of these deserve separate mention.

Papermaking

This had died before the century was out but it had a history extending over 100 years. The first mill was at Danescombe above the valley of that name and was making coarse brown paper, paste and millboard as early as 1788. The 6-in Ordnance map still marks the leat which brought power to the mill's overshot water-wheel. A Sun Assurance policy with the date 16 May 1788 provides the first traceable mention of the mill, which is next heard of when advertised for sale in the *Exeter Flying Post* (26 September 1811). It was then described as carrying on a brown paper business and having one large vat 'and all the fixed machinery constructed on the best principles'. Paper mills until the middle of the nineteenth century were compelled to have an excise licence (that for the Danescombe Mill was numbered 51) and Peter Hill 'a manufacturer of coarse brown papers at Calstock' figured in a law case in 1825, successfully rebutting a charge of being in possession of more paper at the Danescombe Mill than his excise return stated.

In 1851 the mill was working with one vat and a beating engine, and appears to have been in production off and on until 1857.[8] A

somewhat bigger and more interesting mill was situated immediately above Gunnislake Bridge on the river's Cornish bank on a
site marked today by a garage. When it first started making paper is
uncertain but in 1854 it was offered for sale (with the recommenda-
tion that it could be adapted as a flour mill) as a building four storeys
high housing a cutting machine and 'two large and exceedingly
powerful pairs of finishing rollers with cast iron frames erected at
great cost and on the newest principle'. The third and first floors
were used as drying lofts. This mill could make 100 tons of paper
and millboard a year and was powered by a 30 ft × 6 in undershot
water-wheel driven by water from a channel cut from the Tamar.[9]
At one time peat was cut near Princetown for the mill, paper being
made from the fibres. It was badly damaged by fire in 1866 and
appears subsequently to have been turned into lodging tenements
and was variously known as 'Caledonia' or 'Klondyke'. The
building was demolished in the 1920s.

Brick and Tile Making

Except at one small and isolated works not a single traditional-
type building brick is made in Cornwall today, but between 1870
and 1900 Calstock was producing more building bricks, vitrified
fire bricks, fireclay linings and tiles than any other centre west of
Lee Moor. The 'fireclay' they were made from derives from a de-
composed elvan (a hard rock of igneous origin) which outcrops at
Hingston Down and is stained reddish with iron. Farther on towards
Gunnislake the elvan becomes sandy and was used for a softer type
of brick. In 1750 Dr Richard Pococke in his *Travels through England*
noted a coarse-earthenware manufactory using this or a similar type
of clay at Calstock, but the manufacture of bricks and tiles in the
district only began in earnest with the repeal of the tax on bricks in
1850[10]. Among the earliest works were those at Bealeswood just
below Gunnislake. They fronted the river where the bricks were
loaded directly on to barges from a small quay. Blue 'heavy duty'

bricks were made here in large quantities for 'government work', and in 1857 they were being offered at 35s a thousand. Two years later the Sand Hill brickworks owned by B. Johns & Company of Gunnislake were offering a 'superior firebrick for blast and smelting purposes' as well as 'lumps and squares and sifted fireclay'.

The real development of the industry came, however, with the virtual exhaustion by the late 1860s of the Stourbridge clay deposits in Worcestershire which had been the principal source for firebrick clays. These deposits were of high quality, but Hingston Down when prospected towards the end of the 1860s was found to yield a clay comparing very favourably with them. By the middle 1870s over 400 people were employed, 'and more orders were being obtained than could be fulfilled'[11]. The transformation on Hingston Down was extraordinary. A bleak, peaty and hitherto featureless waste above St Ann's chapel glinted and glowed by night with the fires of kiln furnaces, while by day the down was full of labour gangs digging and wheeling away the red-pigmented clay to crushing and kneading mills.

In this way the Calstock Firebrick Company,* the Phoenix Vitrified Paving & Firebrick Works, the Tamar Firebrick & Clay Company, the West of England Bitumen and Chymical [sic] Company and the Plymouth Fireclay Company all sprang up within four years. They turned out thousands of linings for Admiralty boiler furnaces, gas retorts, crucibles, heavy duty 'blue' bricks (principally used in engineering works where great strength was necessary), and vitrified paving bricks for tiling yards, mews and slaughter houses, as well as highly glazed terra-cotta tiles in a variety of designs. Most of the kilns were of the then comparatively new continuous-burning Hoffman type, less wasteful of heat than the old up-draught kiln.

The Phoenix works, erected in 1874 for £60,000, established an

---

* A reminder of the Calstock works today are two beehive-shaped kilns, with their stack, standing in a field by a farm adjoining Hingston Down Mine.

extensive trade with the Russians, who were said to have highly esteemed Hingston Down bricks, and in July 1875 a large delivery of Phoenix bricks was shipped from Calstock to Cronstadt naval dockyard near St Petersburg[12]. Nine years later the company terminated its lease, concentrating its works at Wellington in Somerset where bricks are still made. Mystery envelops the end of the Phoenix Works which adjoin the old Sevenstones Halt on Hingston Down. They are said to have been abandoned when the machinery collapsed. Only a few skeletal arches standing by the railway line to Callington mark where the kiln ovens once stood.

Within a stone's throw of the Phoenix works and on the same side of the road from Cox's Park to Chilsworthy are the much more extensive remains of the Tamar Firebrick & Clay Company. Built in 1873 and spreading over $4\frac{1}{2}$ acres they were capable of producing 80,000 firebricks a week[13]. The quarry from which they dug their clay can be seen on the opposite side of the road, and was connected to the works by a tramway carrying hand-propelled trolleys. The sixteen kilns could each contain 12,000 bricks, and the flues ran into a chimney-stack 150 ft high. A siding connected the works with the East Cornwall Mineral Railway. Substantial remains of the Tamar works exist today, particularly the polygonal drying-house, which was 120 ft across and three storeys high; it can best be seen from the railway. Production seems to have ceased about 1914, but the tall chimney-stack which dominated the landscape was not removed until the 1930s. Now a caravan park covers part of the site.

One of the pioneers of brick and tile making in Calstock was Thomas Westlake[14], who in addition to a factory at Calstock took over the Gunnislake Bealeswood works until he concentrated production at his Rumleigh factory near Bere Alston. At Rumleigh a deposit of boulder clay produced a finer-quality brick. Isolated on a neck of land almost cut off by flooded meadows, these works were subsequently used for arsenic refining, and with their tall stack

remain today largely intact. Brick and tile making continued in a
small way around Gunnislake and Calstock until the 1930s when it
was killed by the growing use of cement blocks.

Transient, bizarre and now a largely forgotten episode in Calstock's industrial history, the 'fireclay boom' on Hingston Down
was while it lasted a valuable alternative source of employment for
out-of-work miners, even though brickmaking had special skills of
its own. It was a boom that had ended by 1900. The production of
bricks and tiles after that date was never a serious industry, chiefly
because of high transport costs and the remoteness of the production
plants from large centres of demand; this explains why the Phoenix
works was not rebuilt after its machinery had 'collapsed' in the late
1890s.

Shipbuilding

A number of ships have been built on the Tamar between Calstock and Gunnislake. In the 1820s a paddle-wheel steamer was
constructed immediately below Gunnislake bridge, but on a site
lost today and by a builder unknown. A schooner was built and
launched at Calstock in the 1830s and between then and 1860 a
'steamboat, two sloops and five large river boats' were built[15].

The steamboat was probably the old iron paddle-wheel steamer
Emperor built in 1846 for the Calstock & Devonport Steam
Packet Company; she continued in service on the river until the
1870s. Brooming and Robert May built and repaired a number of
25 to 80 ton barges, among them the still-remembered *Edward and
Sarah Brooming*. These were the river's maids-of-all-work, carrying
all the lime, stone, coal and grain traffic. The Tamar barges had a
distinctive rig, which usually consisted of a single mast, a mainsail
and a foresail, with sometimes a jib and gaff topsail.

Calstock's heyday as a small boatbuilding centre, however, was
between 1880 and the first world war, when the Goss Brothers took
over the yard on the Devon bank previously occupied by Edward

Brooming. The 'yard' was in fact no more than a mud bank with a tumbledown shed for shelter which still exists close by the viaduct. The Goss brothers' story begins at Netstakes Quay, just below Weir Head, farther up the river from Calstock, where Emanuel Crocker, who came from North Devon, had earlier set up as a boatbuilder. Netstakes Quay has vanished, but on what today is a deserted stretch of the river bank Crocker, using timber from the surrounding woods, built about five vessels; of only one has any substantial record been preserved. This was the *Tamar Queen*, a 100 ton schooner launched from Netstakes on 15 December 1864. She was 83 ft long, carvel built, and took to the river fully rigged. *Tamar Queen* was a local ship in a way unimaginable today. She was built for Messrs Bowhay, Brighton, Reed & Company of Calstock, who described themselves as shipowners, but her original registration particulars show eighteen people holding sixty-four shares in her. Between them they make up a remarkable cross-section of the commercial life of the district, for they included builders, farmers, merchants, a miner, an innkeeper and a master mariner, all living virtually within hailing distance of the shipbuilder's quay[16].

Tamar Queen was largely employed on the fruit run between Plymouth and Portugal, and fate was to give her a certain notoriety. In 1866 when just out of Lisbon another schooner found her drifting 'with her ensign at half mast and union down'. Seeing no signs of life the crew boarded her, and found that the master, Henry Tremills, of Plymouth, and an able seaman had been killed by a Portuguese member of the crew who had run amok with a meat-axe. In turn he had been despatched by the *Tamar Queen's* crew with a marlinspike. This crew on arrival at Plymouth were charged with murder on the high seas, but were acquitted, a piece of evidence in their favour being the disclosure that the *Tamar Queen* was a teetotal ship. In 1907 the vessel became a total loss after being stranded at Ringbar, off County Cork.

Crocker may have built other boats at Netstakes Quay, although no record of them survives. But one of his employees was his nephew, James Goss, who could barely read or sign his name, but by 1900 he had established a widely known shipbuilding yard at Calstock. On that reclaimed mud bank near the viaduct James Goss and his two brothers built the 60- and 70-ton river barges *Britannia*, *Comet*, *Indus* and *Lillie*, a 150-ton schooner, and smaller boats for the Admiralty and for rowing clubs.

The Goss boats were handmade. Most of their timber was selected by Goss himself from the nearby Cotehele estate and it was then handsawn down to ½-in board in a saw pit close to the yard. This sawing often went on for days from dawn to dark, and when in hot weather the sweat and friction rubbed the sawyers' armpits raw, fuller's earth was dabbed on them. Goss never used a pencil on timber, but indicated the measurements with a scratch of his thumbnail, and their accuracy was never in question.

In this way he built the ketch *C.F.H.* of about 100 tons for a Devon timber merchant from oak, larch and elm blown down on the Cotehele estate in the 1891 blizzard[17]. Goss's barges were about 65 tons dead weight and cost between £400 and £800. They were usually built to the order of a local owner who hired them out by the day or week. The pride of the shipyard, however, was the *Garlandstone*, 150 tons and the last ketch to be launched on the Tamar. She was built as a speculation for £560 and launched in 1909 with her sails furled. Fitted in 1914 with an engine, she traded regularly in the Bristol Channel up to 1959, when she was bought for conversion into a yacht—the last of the wooden Tamar-built merchant vessels to survive[18].

Virtually only the sails, which usually came from Southampton or Plymouth, were bought away from Calstock. All the ropes for mooring, hoisting, towing and rigging were made in a ropeworks at Calstock, which once made a rope 960 ft long and weighing 2 tons for Devon Great Consols mine.

The coming of the railway in 1908 and the first world war six years later killed shipbuilding on the Tamar. During the war the Goss yard made 14 ft and 16 ft skiff dinghies and 20 ft cutters for the Admiralty, which were ferried across the Tamar and put on rail trucks for Newcastle. Watermen's boats, and six-oared gigs which competed in regattas at Looe, Saltash and Calstock and made at a cost of about £1 a foot were built in the early 1920s, the last work of a yard which finally closed in the 1930s. Old 'father Goss' as he was known lived to be 94—dying in 1948. Short, stocky, and immensely strong, he could bend a 6-in nail in his hand, and had a blunt sense of humour. His eye was keen to the last. He used no precision instruments, all his drawings being done in pencil on a big piece of board propped up against the kitchen wall. His boats took his name far beyond Calstock.

Quarrying

Quarrying has been carried on around Calstock for several centuries, mainly at Kit Hill, Hingston Down and Gunnislake. The Kit Hill and Gunnislake quarries produced most of the granite for heavy constructional and ornamental work in the south of England, while that on Hingston Down produced an elvan stone for road making and repairs. Today the only quarry in the area is the eleven-acre working at Chilsworthy, probably the biggest source of road-stone in the West of England. The Kit Hill Quarry, which was connected by an incline to the East Cornwall Mineral Railway, has not worked for a number of years.

Of all the former quarries in the area (and the 1880 Ordnance Survey map shows nine within a half a mile of Gunnislake), probably the most characteristic in its manner of working and in the granite it produced was Pearson's quarry, whose closure soon after 1900 is still remembered for the severe unemployment it brought. It is halfway down the hill which runs through Gunnislake. Opened in 1808, it was celebrated for a hard, fine-grained stone resembling

Aberdeen granite in colour and texture. This was much sought after by public-works contractors and was used in parts of Devonport Dockyard, the nineteenth-century fortifications around Plymouth (providing the faces for most of the gun casements), Blackfriar's Bridge and a large number of street works in Hammersmith, Kensington and Chelsea. Blocks, monumental slabs and pillars, kerbstones and 'pitches' for street paving were produced. The quarry reached the peak of its prosperity late in the last century, when it secured a number of important public contracts, among them one for supplying the stone for Dover breakwater.

Pearson's quarry (the name derives from a former owner) was worked in two sections, the smaller or dry quarry—where the granite was at shallower depths—adjoining the larger or main quarry. Originally a half mile of 3 ft 6 in gauge track was built to carry the granite to Gunnislake station. This was converted to 4 ft $8\frac{1}{2}$ in gauge in 1908 and worked by two engines *Tamar* and *Cornwall* to Gunnislake where the former East Cornwall Mineral Railway, also then converted, took it to Calstock Quay. Here steamers and 500-ton 'flats', all named after precious stones, took it to a variety of destinations in southern England.

Cornish granite is found in larger and more regular masses or beds than the finer-grain granite of other areas, and this makes it cheaper to work. At Pearson's quarry it was excavated with picks and steel wedges and occasionally by blasting, which had to be undertaken with great caution because of the nearness of the workings to the houses and the road. The granite, which is hard enough to blunt the chisels of modern pneumatic drills, was in the last century split by hand drills or augers known as 'jumpers'[19]. The 'jumper' was held and rotated between the hands by one man while two others hit it alternately with heavy sledges, and as the boring tool sprang up and down under the rhythm of the blows it made a ringing sound similar to a peal of bells. After splitting the stone was cut, fashioned and polished by hand. A skilled worker could cut

10 ft of kerbstone from a rough granite block in one day or fashion seventy to eighty paving stones weighing nearly a ton.

By the end of the century Pearson's quarry was employing nearly 700 men. A solid belt of granite had been excavated to a depth of 130 ft in places. The quarry was nearly a quarter of a mile wide and the lowest levels could only be reached by climbing down three forty-bar ladders lashed together. Despite a pump working day and night, water was so troublesome that there was a serious proposal at one time to drive a level underneath Gunnislake to drain it into the river at Weir Head.

The project was killed by a chronic shortage of money and the outbreak of war. By 1914 the quarry had been closed because of increasing difficulty in obtaining stone and a falling off in orders. No granite has been taken since. The railway, partly carried across the floor of the huge excavation on spectacular granite piers, was dismantled in 1915 and the offices, blacksmith's shop and storerooms allowed to fall into ruin. Today it is a huge lake of inky-black water, an astonishing memorial to over 100 years of toil—a memorial unknown and unseen by thousands who pass it on their way to Cornwall's beaches in the summer[20].

Of Calstock's other industries, tanning and brewing were carried out on a small scale at Harrowbarrow and Albaston. The brewery was demolished fifty years ago, and the site is now a walled garden. Calstock's short-lived foundry was the Tamar Iron Works, belonging in 1854 to Bowhay, Sims & Company. It incorporated a hammer mill which in 1854 was advertising for a 'hammer man and shovel maker' who was promised 'constant work and liberal wages'.

Like Morwellham, Calstock finally succumbed to the railway. When in 1908 it was given a direct rail link with Plymouth and other centres, the busy barge traffic which had sustained the port however severe the slump in mining, was superseded and Calstock lost its independent trade. Since then the symbols of its energetic past—the leaning chimney, deserted mine buildings, the gaunt granite quarry and the overgrown spoil-heaps rich in specimens for the mineralogist—have claimed more attention than its present needs. Even its ferry, the one tenuous link with its historic past, ceased to ply in 1967, giving Cremyll ferry near Plymouth the distinction of remaining the last of the ancient 'passages' of the Tamar.

HALTON QUAY

Three miles below Calstock, where the Tamar begins to make its last great loop before broadening to its estuary, is Halton Quay, once among the prosperous trading points on the river's lower reaches. It provided easy access from Cornwall to the lead and silver mines around Bere Ferrers, and as a quay and steamer-embarkation or landing point it was the outlet for the produce from some of the richest farm and market-garden land in the Tamar Valley. From Halton Quay straight paths and tracks run half-hidden between deep flower-decked banks to Hingston Down and Calstock, for so greatly does the Tamar 'wind and return upon itself in most tortuous fashion' that it was often quicker to send granite direct from Hingston Down to this quay for shipment to Plymouth and other places along the coast than to take it to Calstock for loading on barges.

Today the reminders of the settlement which trade attracted to the quay are a row of Georgian cottages and a block of lime kilns standing up bluff and square to the river like a castle keep. Packhorse and wagon teams were kept permanently stabled at Halton Quay and their quarters with the hayloft over them still exist. When in 1850 tenements on the quay were offered for auction they included a now-vanished licensed house, four lime kilns, a malt house with a separate kiln, coal and timber yards and an ore yard used until about 1856 for stacking for shipment mineral ores brought by horse transport from mines in Linkinghorne parish. In the 1840s and 50s when the mines on the Bere peninsula were active, residents could set their clocks by the bells of the count-houses at Lockeridge, Furzehill and Whitsom mines across the river, 'calling up the night core men and calling down the forenoon core men' to their places. The ferry between the shores was the chief means of transport.

Halton Quay closed in 1926. Difficulties about renewing leases led to the establishment of Kelly Bray as an agricultural supply depot for East Cornwall, and from then on road and rail transport took over the trade of the last active quay on the Tamar.

OTHER QUAYS

Some remaining quays must have briefer mention. *Hole's Hole* (probably a corruption of Hall's hole) and *Weir Quay* are 2 miles down from Halton and stand on the Devon bank of the Tamar where it begins to straighten its course for Plymouth. Hole's Hole can be used at all states of the tide, and was favoured for the despatch of flowers or fruit to the Plymouth market. Weir Quay is a deep-water berth and has a centuries-old link with the Tamar silver-lead mines. It was the unloading point for all the South Wales coal used by the mines and smelting-houses on the Bere Alston peninsula as well as for parcels of ore from abroad (see Chapter Three).

Opposite Weir Quay is *Cargreen*, with its wide main street leading straight to the river's edge. This was an important Tamar passage abandoned through changing marketing trends after the first world war. Cargreen in medieval times traded in cured Tamar salmon, and shared with Landulph a number of coastal shipping enterprises. To prevent smuggling a revenue cutter was regularly stationed here in the eighteenth century. *Landulph*, below Cargreen, at a point where the Tamar is joined by the Tavy, had its moments of glory in the fifteenth century, for from here in 1434 and subsequent years pilgrims took ship to the shrine of St James of Compostella in Santiago.

It nearly became a spa of sorts in the nineteenth century, when a clergyman had the idea of popularizing a mineral spring where the water had iron properties. But the river overwhelmed the embankment he had built to enclose the low-lying land round the spring, and Landulph relapsed into obscurity. Its quay is still marked on the map and so is that of *Moditanham* just below it, now also crumbling and disused, a relic of the times when lime was burnt on the foreshore nearby.

Most of the quays mentioned above were historically important in their own right long before the nineteenth century brought them a renewed prosperity. But others, like forgotten *Newquay* (originally New Quay) and *Gawton* between Morwellham and Calstock, had humbler beginnings. Newquay began in the eighteenth century as an insignificant collecting and distributing point for the Duke of Bedford's tenant farmers. Its principal building was then a small store shed, but by 1850 its quay space had been greatly enlarged to take the surplus copper ore of Devon Great Consols mine. Gawton Quay began as a wharf to serve Gawton copper mine, which can be seen from Newquay; by 1860 these two quays formed an almost continuous frontage along the river for nearly a quarter of a mile.

Newquay expanded into a settlement with its own inn and quay overseer, and became the postal address for the registered offices of at least one mining company. Today its nearest inhabited house is half a mile away. This quay, as a later chapter will show, became one of the principal lime-burning centres for the farmlands west of Tavistock. Gawton remained largely a mineral quay, exporting arsenic and copper ore until the pumps of Bayly's and King's shafts from which Gawton mine was worked stopped for good in 1901. Very often these quays held considerable stores. When the firm leasing Gawton held an auction there in 1858 it offered for sale a portable 6-ton crane, eighteen horses with wagons and carts stabled on the quay, 250 tons of iron and large quantities of coal, slate, salt, white and red lead, tallow, manure and timber. Isolated and

51

Calstock in the early years of this century, with Goss's shipyard in the foreground

Calstock viaduct in 1905. Note the shipping round the piers

The viaduct, circa 1907, and within a few months of its completion

The ketch Garlandstone *on the stocks at Goss's shipyard. Members of the Goss family are under its bows*

ruined, Newquay and Gawton today could easily be passed unnoticed on the river.

Impham Quay, on the Devon bank of the Tamar between Gunnislake and Morwellham, has vanished. Here tin, granite, manganese
and fireclay were once shipped and barges manœuvred to make the
'Impham turn' to tie up alongside. It probably existed in the seven-
teenth century, and in 1869 it was the principal outlet for granite
from Frementor Quarry, an isolated and now-abandoned granite
working adjoining Devon Great Consols mine. The quarry was
connected to the quay by a 2½-mile horse tramway so badly constructed in places as 'not to admit of a large amount of traffic being
drawn over it'. The traffic was indeed short-lived, less on account
of the rickety railway than because the Frementor granite splintered
so easily that it was virtually impossible to quarry blocks of suitably
large size. Parts of the tramway are still marked on the 2½-in map.
Tuckermarsh Quay, north-west of Bere Alston, still preserves its
name but has lost its trade.

Cotehele Quay is a good spot to end this survey, for it stands today
carefully preserved by the National Trust—a curious compound,
like the Valley itself, of nineteenth-century industrial enterprise and
sylvan beauty. It was much used by the soft-fruit trade of the Tamar
Valley at the end of the last century, but in earlier years considerable
quantities of copper ore and arsenic were exported through it. In
1819 it was advertised for sale, with its lime kilns, warehouses,
granaries, cellars and stabling, as 'a very large and commodious quay
with a most desirable situation on the river'. Traffic considerably
increased after September 1864 when the Earl of Mount Edgcumbe
opened a new road from Callington to it. The want of a good road
had been severely felt in 1837 when a dismantled 30-in engine was
transferred from a barge at the quay to Wheal Brothers mine near
Callington over roads which caused far more difficulty than the sea
passage from Truro.*

* D. B. Barton, *The Cornish Beam Engine*, p. 123.

D

CHAPTER THREE

Silver and Lead

THE silver-lead mines of the Tamar Valley have probably been more profitably worked over a longer period than any other mines in England. They financed some of the martial enterprises of the Plantagenet kings. Nobody knows when or how they were discovered, but in the reign of Edward I they are mentioned as mines in full production, and it is clear from the amount of silver being taken that they had been developed over a number of years.

Their silver and lead have come from two strongly marked lead lodes coursing north and south through the Bere Alston peninsula[1]. Traced on a map, these appear as two straight lines running parallel about three-quarters of a mile apart. On the shorter or western lode which skirts the Tamar there are three mines—Ward, North Hooe and South Hooe. The adjoining and longer eastern lode, which appears to have been the first discovered, has been worked from five mines—Butspill, Lockeridge, Furzhill, East Tamar and South Tamar Consols. The lead ore in them had a high silver content which was richest near the surface; at deeper levels lead predominated. Some of the Bere mines, as they were collectively known, returned between 80 and 100 oz and even as much as 140 oz to the ton. The ore was remarkably free from impurities and in some workings was found associated with fluorspar, mined in considerable quantities in the 1870s for the manufacture of glass. None of the mines has been worked since the 1880s and their total yield is never likely to be known. Over several hundred years the figures are probably far in excess of those usually given.

The discovery of the Bere mines is usually put at about 1290 and probably came about through workmen digging up stones 'very bright and the colour like unto lead'. The value of the find was quickly understood, and the king, who by medieval custom rather than by any clearly defined prerogative claimed ownership of all metalliferous mines, seized the newly mined silver for his own treasury. Thus between the 'twelfth daie of August and the last of October' 1294, only four years after the mines are first mentioned, 370 lb of silver ore was sent to the king from Martinstowe (Maristow) on the Tavy, where there was probably some sort of quay, and by 1297 silver worth £4,046 and probably representing some 70 lb in weight, as well as £360 worth of lead, had been sent to the royal treasury from workings that could have been little more than shallow pits. One little-known link with the medieval mines is in Shillamill Wood, near Crowndale. Here are fragmentary remains of a leat running a little below the 400 ft contour, tunnelled in places through rock cut by chisels before gunpowder was in use. A Tavistock Abbey document of 1461 refers to this leat which was about 20 miles long and probably brought water from the river Lumburn to those mines nearest the Tavy.

Except for the silver mines of Combe Martin[2] in North Devon, the only other mining activity in Devon and Cornwall at this time was the shovelling of tin from alluvial deposits. This called for no great labour force or organized skill. Silver, on the other hand, needed working at deeper levels and it was harder to extract. To obtain enough suitable men, by 1295 the king was impressing under royal warrant 340 miners 'out of the Peak in Derbyshire' to make the twelve-days' journey to Devon, while others were later sent from Wales. The impressment system continued at intervals throughout the fourteenth century, enforced with summary powers; any man who refused to make the journey to Devon could be imprisoned until he found a security to serve in his place.

In 1299 one of the half-dozen mines working in the area was pledged by the king to financiers of the Florentine company of the Frescobaldi, the Italian financial counterpart of the German Fug-

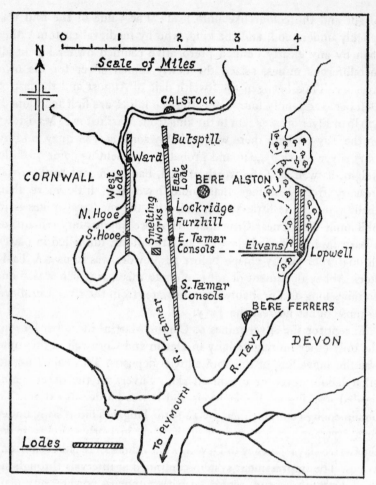

The Bere Alston silver-lead lodes

gers; but it was not the best of their bargains. The ore proved poor
and the cost of hauling it out of all proportion to the original estimates. Within six years (1305) the mines were back in royal hands,
and, significantly, a record amount of £1,775 worth of silver and

£810 worth of lead was obtained. This appears to have come from four mines—the South Mine, Middle Mine, Fershull (the present Furzhill) and the Old Mine. The exact number of mines working at this time is unknown but a reference in 1453 refers to 'six pits or shafts at Bere Ferrers reserved exclusively for the king's use'.

Under the spur of the king's demands and the high wages that could be earned, some of the most experienced miners in Europe were attracted to the Bere mines, and this concentration of skilled labour brought advances in techniques. The chief of these was the method of draining the mines by 'avidots' or levels pierced into the sides of the 400–500-ft flat-topped ridge between the Tamar and Tavy along whose summit the mines were first opened. This process appears to have been introduced into the Bere mines about 1297, for in that year William Peppercorn and his partners and six other gangs received payments averaging £12 10s for making the 'avidots' or adits. The Bishop of Chester reported in 1298 that the yield of the Bere mines had been doubled because work was now being carried on in winter as well as summer. By 1480 winding hooks are being mentioned, which suggests that shaft mining had begun some time previously—it could not have started much before this in any other mine in the country.

The mines seem to have been the king's concern throughout much of the fourteenth century, although their boom years were in the half-century 1290–1340. They were also let from time to time to private adventurers, although few fortunes appear to have been made. The output in the fifteenth century fluctuated wildly. In 1426 only 30 oz had been produced in two and a half years, but for the six years 1445–51 the average output of silver rose to 4,000 oz. In 1480 there was still a comparatively large labour force, next heard of along with the men of Combe Martin in 1485, when 1,000 are said to have been employed; but this figure probably covered the two areas. For a few years after this date the mines are said to have yielded £44,000 a year to the king, but by the end of the century

increasing depths and difficulty with water led to them being tem-
porarily abandoned, although 'abounding very much in silver lead'.

There are many tantalizing gaps in the early history of these
mines. While there is incidental information about their working,
there is nothing about their depth, or how the miners lived, or
whether those who came from the North and from Wales inter-
married with the local population. Was it the wealth of the silver
mines and the large working population they attracted which led
Sir Richard de Ferrers between 1330 and 1333 to endow Bere
Ferrers church with an archpriest, four other priests and a deacon,
living as a community—an otherwise extraordinary superfluity of
prelates in one parish[3]? The mines could hardly have been un-
affected by the Black Death, because it depopulated settlements
around Tavistock and in one year (1355) there were no coinage
returns because of its ravages. Yet enough survives to make plain
that on this little peninsula in the Tamar Valley there flourished for
nearly 200 years the most highly organized mining community in
Southern England and one of the most advanced experiments in
medieval industrial enterprise in the British Isles.

More people then worked in the peninsula than do today. Bere
Alston became a borough (shortly after 1295), with a market in
which miners were prohibited from loitering on the pretence of
purchasing meat. The river was thick with the traffic of a boom
area. Silver loaded and stored in canvas bags was shipped to Plymouth. Timber came down the river in barges from the woods
around Calstock, and along with it oak-bark refuse from the tanners,
which was used as an absorbent material for refining the silver[4].
There was a constant traffic to and from Plymouth and Tavistock,
and to the quays at Maristowe, Weir Quay and Hole's Hole with
supplies of iron for making tools, hides for bellows, leather buckets
and pump suckers (all of which were made on the mine), winding
hooks, sea coal from Newcastle for the forges, canvas bags for carrying the ore, Normandy ropes, shovels and other utensils.

Smelting was done on the spot. The first crude smelting struc-
tures, like lime kilns in appearance, were put up in 'draughty places'
on the ridge to catch the wind and thus force the fires. These were
later superseded by 'slag hearths' resembling blacksmith's furnaces,
forced draught being supplied by bellows actuated by a water-
wheel. The silver (the ore was broken by hand) seems to have been
cast into plates or ingots varying from 10 to 20 pounds weight in and
value—the monetary pound being simply the pound weight of standard silver. Working on the mine sites were smelters, blacksmiths,
pitmen, carpenters, sawyers, sorters, ore washers, pumpmen, clerks
and foremen. No significant advance from the mining techniques
practised here in the fifteenth century was made until gunpowder
came to be generally used in the middle 1600s, and the steam pumping engine sixty years later. In fact the only thing a nineteenth-
century miner would have missed would have been the hiss of a
steam engine.

As already said, the men were among the best paid in the country,
their wage being as high as or higher than the average paid to
skilled artisans anywhere. Thus Simon Russell worked for thirty-
four days as a miner at 4d a day, but his ore washing brought him
in £7 12s 11d and work as a water-winder 7s, making £8 11s 3d,
earned in what was considerably less than a working year. William
Martin, working 221 days as a miner and fifty-three as a water-
winder, received £4 11s 6d, while another received 14s 2d for smelting 170 bowls of ore at 1d a bowl. To gain some idea of the present-
day value of these payments the amount must be multiplied 120
times.

In addition, as employees of the king the miners were to a certain
extent apart from the law and free from special tolls and taxes.
For most offences they were answerable to a warden, who administered a code of penalties. These do not appear to have been
too harsh. To constrain the 'contrairient and rebellious' a pit was
dug in 1302 'by way of prison', but this punishment lacked the

savage overtones accompanying medieval justice in some other
mining areas.

<h2>THE NINETEENTH-CENTURY REVIVAL</h2>

For nearly 200 years until the beginning of the nineteenth century
the Bere mines remain in obscurity. The primitive smelting methods
of earlier days left a good deal of silver in the slag and there seem
to have been attempts in Elizabeth's day to rework this. There was
an unsuccessful effort to reopen them in Charles II's time. After
this they disappear until between 1784 and 1785 the South Hooe
mine on the western lode is recorded as producing 6,500 oz of
silver out of ore containing 140 oz of silver to the ton—one of the
richest pockets of ore ever to be found in the district. The mines
were then worked by Christopher Gullett of Tavistock, a versatile
personality who besides speculating in neighbouring mines was
deputy clerk of the peace for Devon, took out a patent for a hydraulic
engine in 1773 and capped it twenty years later with a remedy for
the gout[5]. Yet the mines were not well known at this time. Westcote
ignores them, as does John Donne's map of Devon, published in
1756, although he marks a copper and tin working to the north of
them. Nor are they shown on Greenwood's map of Plymouth, which
appeared in 1824, although it illustrates the Bere Alston peninsula
in detail.

Nevertheless by 1809 these ancient mines had resumed their
place among the leading lead and silver producing workings in
the kingdom. Steam power enabled the workings to be extended to
the rich pockets of silver under the bed of the Tamar, and for the
next forty years over 1,000 people were employed[6]. The two chief
workings were the South Hooe mine on the western lode, possibly
the richest in the area, which under the management of Percival
Norton Johnson became linked with important technical and smelt-

ing developments, and South Tamar Consols on the adjoining eastern lode—a mine only slightly less rich but which achieved notoriety by being overwhelmed one Sunday evening by the Tamar.

The South Hooe mine is marked on the 6-in map and is situated on a shelf in a hillside about 100 ft above the Tamar and half a mile up the river from Hole's Hole. Its main shaft was 50 yd in from the river and was eventually sunk to 250 fathoms, the workings finally extending over a quarter of a mile south of the river. Today three walls of an engine house, the outlines of a large pond which supplied water to the pumping-engine and dressing-floors, and the ruins of its count-house with a large bay window from which the mine captain auctioned the pitches, are all that remain.

It was moribund when it was acquired in 1835 by the Tamar Silver Lead Company of which Johnson was the leading director. He became general manager of the mine and one of the first benefits of his control was the installation—unusual at the time in metalliferous mines in this country—of a system of fan ventilation, by which fumes from shot firing were sucked 200 ft to the surface in $1\frac{1}{2}$ minutes. The fan, worked at first intermittently by hand and later by a water-wheel, drew air through a wooden duct $4\frac{1}{2}$ in by $5\frac{1}{2}$ in which ran 280 fathoms into the mine.

The richest lodes of South Hooe lay under the Tamar, and to reach these Johnson began in 1843 the sinking of a new inclined shaft angled at 25 degrees for easy hauling and to allow men to walk along it without the toil of using ladders—a typical example of Johnson's forethought and unusual at that date. It was sunk slowly down to 125 fathoms and well out under the Tamar, but the depth was found to be beyond the capacity of the hauling-engine in use. Another engine, of 20 horse power, was installed, 115 fathoms underground in a chamber dug out of the rock under the river, from which a vertical shaft led down another 360 ft. This engine, known as Spurgin's after one of the mine's directors, drew up ore from the vertical shaft on a consumption 'of only half a crown's worth of coal per 24 hours'. Its fumes and exhaust were led 690 ft to the surface by a flue which wandered through the old and new workings and acquired a legendary reputation for leaking.

The inclined shaft not only provided easier access to the lower levels and better haulage, but so improved ventilation that men had to hold on to their caps in places where previously a candle would not burn for two minutes. The ore in the deepest levels proved well worth the trouble taken to get it, yielding between 50 to 60 oz of silver to the ton and occasional samples of up to 100 oz.

South Hooe's prosperity steadily grew under Johnson's direction. He introduced the German device of shaking-tables for the better dressing and classifying of the ores—probably for the first time anywhere in the South West. By 1852 over 200 people were employed on the mine, and nearly £44,000 had been paid out in dividends on an original outlay of only £12,000. There were seven steam engines on the property, one of them a 50-in pumping-engine with three boilers. The mine was worked in conjunction with the adjoining North Hooe mine the two being known together as *Tamar Consols*.

Ores from Tamar Consols were smelted at Weir Quay. In 1845 Johnson's company acquired the works, which had been in existence before the 1830s, and re-equipped them; the Tamar smelting works became one of the leading centres for smelting lead and silver ores. The eighteen furnaces could smelt well over 300 tons of lead ore a month and employed between 80 and 90 men. The deep-water berth at Weir Quay, adjoining the works, was improved to take vessels of up to 400 tons, and these brought in ore for smelting from Spain, France, Newfoundland and Wales. The lead ore was first partly roasted in a calcining furnace, where it was mixed with lime which served as a flux. It was then treated at higher temperatures in other furnaces to recover its silver content. The waste was converted back into lead, and cast into saleable ingots. In 1850 the then new Pattinson process of smelting was introduced, enabling silver

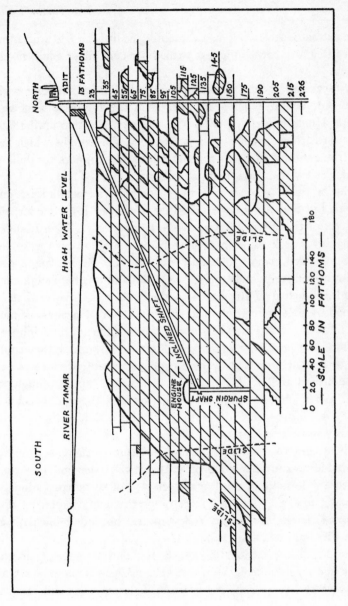

Section of South Tamar or Hooe Mine

to be extracted from lead ores containing as little as 3 to 4 oz a ton; before this, ore containing less than 8 per cent silver could not be treated.

In 1852, much against Johnson's wish, the Tamar smelting works were sold; but he retained an interest in the adjoining somewhat smaller Union smelting works, which remained active until 1896[5]. Afterwards they reopened as a jam factory, the troughs which had held the refining furnaces making admirable coppers for boiling Tamar Valley raspberries and strawberries.

Johnson was by training and inclination a metallurgist and assayer, but his career has similarities to that of John Taylor, the architect of the Tavistock Canal (see Chapter Six). Both founded companies which still bear their name—in Johnson's case the Hatton Garden firm of Johnson Matthey & Co. Both brought new and improved techniques to their work, and a humane, enlightened attitude—unusual at the time—to their workers, 'many of them doomed by pale consumption to an early death'. Numbers of men were blinded by the crude blasting methods of the day, and Johnson sponsored an early form of embossed lettering by which they could learn to read. He built at his own expense a group of cottages and a schoolroom at Bere Alston, and had a water supply brought to them. When cholera raged in Callington and the parish council burnt tar in the streets to ward it off, he and his wife worked tirelessly to relieve distress.

A busy, practical, far-seeing man, Johnson became a substantial shareholder in a number of Devon and Cornwall mines, and he earned himself a fellowship of the Royal Society; but he remains a lonely, enigmatic figure. After his premature retirement, somewhat disillusioned, from his Tamar Valley mines, he ended his days at Stoke Fleming, where he is buried.

After his death, in 1866, the mine he had built up never again saw the prosperity it had enjoyed under his guidance. It ceased working twenty years later. In thirty-one years, between 1845 and 1876, it produced 326,300 oz of silver and over 9,000 tons of lead. If the figures for previous centuries are taken into consideration, the total production of silver was probably well over 600,000 oz, making it easily the richest of the Tamar mines. Between 1879 and 1882, nearly 800 tons of fluorspar was produced, although by this time the mine had become too deep to work economically with the means available. The adjoining North Hooe mine, which had been worked to a depth of 100 fathoms, was reopened in 1906, mainly because its shallow and uncomplicated workings made it easier to explore. The year proved to be exceptionally wet and as the company had insufficient funds to conquer the water below the 70 fathoms level, the project was abandoned. It was the last attempt at underground mining in the peninsula.

One other working on this western lode was *Ward* mine, 1 mile south-east of Calstock on the Devon bank of the river. From 1873-6 it produced 390 oz of silver and 130 tons of lead, but of more immediate interest is its engine-house, which is preserved largely intact today as a farmhouse. The adjoining stack (in what is still called 'stack field') has been demolished, but the fixtures over which the pumping-rods passed to the shaft are still clearly visible. The shaft, 60 fathoms deep, and adjoining the garden path, fell in one Sunday morning, and is now marked by a shallow depression. To the north of the engine-house are the remains of the dressing-floors and some cottages which were once part of the count-house. Ward mine ceased working about 1880 and was never important, but the main outlines of a typical small Tamar Valley silver-lead mine are more clearly preserved here than anywhere else in the district. There is a tradition that the boiler of its 45-in cylinder Cornish engine was towed up the river to Calstock on a raft to do duty for many years as a rainwater tank for a cottage.

The ill-fated *South Tamar Consols* was the richest mine on the adjoining eastern lode and its site can be found about a quarter of a mile south of Weir Quay. Today its solitary chimney, virtually all that remains of it on the surface apart from its dumps, seems to spring out of the hillside close to the river bank. In line with it is a small shallow adit in the roadside bank, through which in dry seasons some of its workings along with those of the adjoining East Tamar mine can be approached.

A tracing made in 1855 of an old chart of this mine notes that some of its deepest workings had not been seen 'since the days of Queen Elizabeth'. By the middle of the last century, however, South Tamar Consols ranked as the second most prosperous mine in the area, and a company formed to work it in the 1840s had in ten years divided £32,000 among its shareholders. Shortly before, it had been valued at £90,000, making each 9s share worth £10. The mine was then being worked under the river between Hole's Hole and Cargreen in ground estimated to contain £80,000 worth of ore. Eight steam engines were used, while nearly 150 men were employed, many in underground workings extending 2½ miles.

All this activity was abruptly ended at 8 p.m. on Sunday, 30 August 1856, when the Tamar burst into the mine at a point where the ground under the river was weakened by a slide—a clay filling in the slate. Water poured into a subsidence 20 ft long by 12 ft wide causing a 'loud report as of thunder' as the expelled air blew off the covers of the closed shafts[8]. Masses of timber were thrown up, and in a few minutes £20,000 worth of damage had been done. Had it happened on a weekday over ninety miners would probably have lost their lives.

The accident let loose a flood of wild rumours and even wilder suggestions for repairing the damage. One miner reported that men had been gradually leaving the mine because they knew it would be drowned; it was alleged there were no adequate plans of the working under the river (this was subsequently disproved) and that the mine captain had turned a deaf ear to repeated warnings. Also revealed incidentally was that there was no inspector of mines for Devon and Cornwall—an omission still unremedied seven years later. Suggestions for sealing the breach included stuffing it with rocks, quick-lime and small coal and isolating it from the river with an iron tube. The superintending engineer of the Royal Albert Bridge at Saltash, which was building at the time, was called in to suggest more practicable methods, but as it was estimated it would take nearly two years and 4,000 tons of coal to pump out the mine, plans for reopening it were abandoned. When the river overwhelmed it not only was a rich course of ore being opened up but 120 tons were lying broken in the levels ready to be brought to surface. In the following December five of South Tamar's steam engines and 417 fathoms of tramway were auctioned off for £6,000 at Plymouth. In eight years between 1852 and 1860 it had produced 262,470 oz of silver. Attempts in 1860 to pick up the lost lode at Cargreen were apparently unsuccessful.

The disaster to South Tamar spelled the doom of the adjoining *East Tamar Consols* whose workings were connected with it. It was able to keep going for a few years by working the ground of the adjoining Lockeridge mine, where in 1856 the 'proprietors cut it exceedingly rich' in opening up a lead lode yielding 15 tons of ore to the fathom. But by March 1861 the 50-in engine was unable to cope with the rising water from the Tamar and it was offered for sale with twenty-one years of its lease still to run[9]. It appears never to have resumed production. This mine has been known as Furzhill and Whitsom Down, and is reputed to have produced nearly 19,000 oz of silver between 1845 and 1861.

Lockeridge or *Goldstreet* mine can be identified today by a chimney-stack near the railway line south of Bere Alston. Its dumps were examined for fluorspar in 1942. From here the lode courses northeast to *Butspill* or *Tamar Valley* mine, deep in a wooded valley by the river and the most northerly of the Bere mines. It was working in Elizabethan times, but its recorded outputs of lead and silver are small. The engine-house, now a dangerous and ivy-mantled ruin, still stands and the dumps, a stone's throw away, still offer good specimens of fluorspar. The mine worked from 1866 to 1876, and in its last six years it produced 650 oz of silver, 620 tons of fluorspar and 20 tons of iron pyrites.

Wheal Jenny marked as such on the six-inch 1906 OS map remains elusively unknown. It may have been the *Queen of the Tamar* lead and silver mine for which there was an advertisement in the PDWJ of 14 June 1860 for coal 'suited for engine purposes' to be delivered at Tuckermarsh Quay. It is marked on the map just east of Tuckermarsh railway bridge about half a mile on the Tavistock side of Bere Alston station. Here there is a wood with a few mounds which may be remains of dumps but there are no records of output.

No mining areas in the South West are more evocative to wander over than the Bere Alston peninsula. Man has groped for lead and silver among its valleys for nearly 700 years and in the last century the mineral was mined and smelted amid cherry orchards and tea gardens to which hundreds of people flocked in paddle steamers from Plymouth. At a conservative estimate the total amount of silver obtained from these mines in the last century probably exceeded a million ounces, along with over 20,000 tons of lead. The only visual evidences of this today are one or two forgotten quays, some leaning chimney-stacks, and grass-grown dumps where specimens of pink and green fluorspar, blende, calcite and banded quartz can still be found.

CHAPTER FOUR

The Lime Trade

THE lime trade is probably the oldest of the Tamar Valley's industries. Barges were bringing sea sand and river-estuary mud for
liming the land long before mining became important, and in later
centuries the winning, burning and transport of limestone continued to be a major industry after many of the local mines had been
forgotten. Bargemen, horse drovers, quarrymen, limeburners and
labourers, using the river as their main channel of communication,
formed a chain from the seashore and the quarry to the fields to give
the farmer the means of making his fields fertile.

THE AGRICULTURAL DEMAND

Lime is one of the oldest soil conditioners known, and a cheap
source of calcium—a vital constituent of plant tissue. The slate
soils of the Tamar Valley are predominately acid, and lime was
essential for a correct soil balance. When woodlands were felled and
valley bottoms cleared, a generous dressing of lime was the best
possible treatment until the introduction of artificial manures early
in the nineteenth century. So the regular liming of pasture and
arable land assumed an almost obsessive importance to landlord and
tenant alike and it was not unusual for leases, particularly in the
eighteenth century, to specify precisely the amount of lime to be
used either as a general 'manure' or for conditioning newly broken
land for wheat.

It also had a multitude of other uses. Wheat was steeped in a
gruel made from lime to prevent 'smut' or fungus. Mixed with

sand, lime made mortar and was the source of all the cement used
in the area until late in the nineteenth century. Powdered lime with
tallow and linseed oil made a waterproof wash for cottages and farm
buildings which stoutly resisted a predominantly damp climate.
Puddled with clay it made a hard lining for cattle ponds. The
tanners and woollen mills used lime for cleansing hides and sheep-
skins, and as lime-water it was even used as a medicine. Next to his
stock and buildings the cost of lime was often the largest item in the
farmer's budget, and any farmer who had a limestone quarry on his
land had the equivalent of a small gold mine. Lime is still important
today in industry and agriculture, and the farmer gets a substantial
subsidy towards its cost. But the lorry has supplanted the stone-
carrying barges that once thronged the river, and the ancient lore of
the lime-burner has vanished beneath the rollers of modern crushing
machinery; this grinds limestone so small that it can be applied
direct, without the need for burning, remaining in the soil for three
or four years. And with the lime-burner have gone, too, the long
lines of patient horse teams that were on the move from his kilns as
the summer dawn was breaking. To find the relics of this vanished
world one must visit the gaunt and silent quarries at Stonehouse and
Cattedown in Plymouth, or pull aside the ivy masking the crumbling
ruggedness of the kilns along the river bank that once burnt day and
night.

There is no limestone in the Tamar Valley[1]. In compensation
nature has provided in Plymouth limestone deposits which run in a
continuous belt for nearly six miles and in one place are a mile in
width. The 'Plymouth marble' as it was sometimes known took on
a high polish and was so rich in calcium that a nineteenth-century
magazine writer doubted if any 'gold mine in the world ever contributed so widely to the prosperity of its vicinity as does the Plymouth limestone'[2]. It is still extracted, from highly mechanized
quarries at Plymstock, which in the year 1963–4 supplied 190,000
tons of lime for agricultural use in Devon and Cornwall.

The practice of using burnt lump lime on the land, however, only became general in Devon towards the end of the eighteenth century. Before then farmers in the Tamar Valley followed the custom of their West Devon and Cornwall neighbours in sweetening their acid soils by massive applications of sea sand. A good sanding for an acre of land was 300 sacks of 16 gallons each. To this dung, seaweed and scrapings from the hedgerows were added. Allied to the practice of beat-burning in which soil weeds, grass roots and stubble were dug up, raked together in heaps and then allowed to burn slowly in the belief that fertilizing properties were released, a tilth was formed which in the hands of the skilled monks of Tavistock Abbey produced corn yields comparable with those from some of the best wheat lands in eastern England. This method of soil preparation did not materially change in the Tamar Valley until the advent of bone and guano fertilizers well after the Napoleonic wars.

Sea sand varies greatly in quality according to its source. On the north coast of Cornwall, at Bude's Summerleaze Beach and Widemouth Bay, over half its weight often consists of calcareous matter. These Bude sands were much sought after by farmers in the northern part of the Tamar Valley. Strings of pack-horses were carrying it to Werrington, above Gunnislake, between 1413 and 1481 at an average cost of 1s 2d for twenty horseloads, and towards the end of the eighteenth century 4,000 horseloads are said to have been taken for agricultural purposes in one day; it became the principal item carried over the Bude Canal.

The sand in the bays around Plymouth, however, and in the estuary of the Tamar is extremely poor in lime, and almost worthless as a manure, although this was not generally understood until late in the eighteenth century; by that time hundreds of thousands of tons of worthless sand, only occasionally enriched with river mud, had almost smothered the soil each side of the Tamar. The carrying of this poor-quality sea sand, 'raised with great toil from different parts of Plymouth Sound' and sent inland 5 or 6 miles in canvas

bags at great expense, had become a lucrative trade on the Tamar
in the thirteenth century. Tavistock Abbey was one of the best
customers, sand for the Abbey lands being brought up the river at
an average price of 6s 8d for a normal barge-load of 14½ tons. In
about 1270 John de Beaupré, steward of the Manor of Trematon,
near Saltash, imposed—among other charges—a toll of 12d a year
upon every sand barge using the Tamar, an action which provoked
a furious outcry. The trade was always peculiarly sensitive to political and economic conditions. Sand which had cost 8s a bargeload
in 1427 had risen to 11s in 1463 as a result of the disturbances
following the reign of Edward IV. It then fell, to remain fairly
steady for several years until 1489, the period of the Breton war and
Perkin Warbeck's invasions, when the price of one bargeload and
one boatload advanced to 12s 6d.

In 1774 the desire for cheaper access to Bude sand led to an Act
being obtained for making a canal from Bude Harbour 'to the Tamar
in Calstock parish for the navigation of boats and other vessels with
heavy burdens'. The Act was allowed to lapse, but a report issued
in 1819, when the idea of a somewhat similar canal was revived,
makes clear that the carriage of sea sand was uppermost in the
promoters' minds. 'Every good farmer exerts himself to bring home
the greatest quantity of sand and every landowner in this district
covenants with a tenant that a certain quantity shall be carried on
every acre broken up for tillage.' The Bude–Calstock canal was
never built, but when the Bude–Launceston waterway was finally
completed it brought down the price of Bude sand at Launceston by
three-quarters.

In the latter half of the eighteenth century farming was becoming
a more exact science. Lime with a more predictable calcium content
than sea sand was demanded and, except in some coastal areas, the
kiln began to replace the sand barge. By 1796 William Marshall in
his *Rural Economy of the West of England* was able to note that a
fleet of mast vessels carrying up to 50 tons was solely employed on

the transport of limestone over the Tamar. By the middle of the nineteenth century the tonnage of limestone carried on the river exceeded that of any other single article.

THE LIME KILNS

Calcium in sea sand is derived from pulverized shells and corals and is inert in water; but lime obtained from limestone is fiercely caustic when wet and quickly destroys soft tissue. For this reason unslaked lime was seldom if ever carried by water; the practice was to burn it in kilns conveniently situated near a river quay.

Most of the kilns now remaining in the Tamar Valley were built between 1770 and 1830 and the sight of them working at almost every quay and landing place impressed travellers almost as much as the woods of Cotehele and Morwell Rocks. Rev William Gilpin in his *Observations on the Western Parts of England* thought the Tamar lime kilns among the noblest ornaments on the river 'which at a little distance might be mistaken for castles'[3]. The Tamar kilns are generally slate built and distinguished by a bold round entrance arch usually keyed with a heavy granite stone. Towards the end of the eighteenth century, when many were over thirty years old, Marshall commented on their 'large and expensive construction some costing not less than £30 and £40 each'.* Usually rectangular and between 20 and 30 ft high, they were approached by a ramp up which a pack horse could walk, a detail to be seen in a number of them today. The lips of the kilns were usually broad enough for a horse to walk round, allowing stone to be unloaded directly into the wells.

Tending these kilns were thirsty and peripatetic personalities—

* He thought the wells tapered too much, however, causing the burnt lime to clog instead of falling easily to the bottom. Marshall was sharply critical of much that he saw in the Tamar Valley.

the lime-burners. They usually lived in a cottage adjoining their kilns, but many of them tended groups of kilns in different districts, staying a week or so at each group until immediate requirements for lime had been satisfied. Like the charcoal-burner, the lime-burner jealously preserved his lore, taught only by experience. Some lime-stones burnt more quickly than others, and the stone from each quarry had its own characteristics.

The lime-burner went about his task after labourers had firmly packed the great wells, often 20 ft or more deep and over 10 ft across, with alternate layers of small coal and limestone. Often in times of heavy demand the limestone would be packed breast-high or more above the top of the kiln, the stone gradually sinking as it burnt. Into the 'eye' or firegrate, usually covered by a heavy iron door, the lime-burner then thrust a bundle of burning birch twigs or furze. The door was shut fast and lime ashes were frequently shovelled around to seal it, for the whole secret lay in burning the stone thoroughly by slow combustion. Half or overburnt lumps remained unslaked in the field, annoyed the farmer and were a poor advertisement of the lime-burner's skill. One ton of Plymouth lime-stone produced 11 cwt of high-quality lime after eight hours in the kiln, and it was scattered over the land at the rate of 3 to 5 tons an acre, a little under half the amount of sand used.

Some kilns were burning almost all the year round, but the busiest times were in autumn and spring. They radiated heat and fumes for yards around and this made lime-burning thirsty work. Until well into the nineteenth century, the cost of drink for the lime-burner was calculated in the price of lime to the farmer. It was not uncommon until the first world war for a farmer to bring a kilderkin of cider for the burner—a two-way traffic which often led to an extra generous bushel measure (a bushel being about $1\frac{1}{2}$ cwt). In cold, wet weather kilns were sociable places to exchange gossip and keep dinners warm; for the homeless and destitute, lime kilns were often havens of warmth and shelter, and cases were not unknown of tramps climbing on to the lip of a kiln to get nearer the warmth, and falling in their sleep to a fiery death.*

Burning lime gives off carbon dioxide and this was widely believed to cause skin complaints. In March 1849 a destitute man was picked up, nearly suffocated, close to a kiln near Plymouth, and a few days later it was reported that 'boils caused by the fumes had broken out on his person'[4]. For country children a visit to a lime kiln was part of the 'cure' for bronchitis and whooping cough; the choking fumes filling the air when a kiln was opened up or 'drawn' were held to 'rack up the phlegm' and so clear the chest.

TRANSPORT OF THE LIMESTONE

Carrying the stone to the kilns was one of the least popular tasks on the river—hard, dirty, meagrely paid work. Barges of between 50 and 60 tons after unloading granite at Plymouth would bring back limestone if no more profitable cargo was available. Cider and beer were inducements offered to get a bargeload of limestone unloaded quickly and sometimes a payment of 3s 6d was offered for three hours' work in unloading a barge which had arrived on the evening tide and was urgently needed for another cargo next day. Stones had to be winched out of the hold with a hand windlass and then carried ashore on a man's shoulder in open bushel baskets. A lighter side of this work was the 'lime feast', an annual dinner or supper which the leading lime merchants gave to their employees, although by the end of the century this custom had died out.

The opening of the Tavistock Canal in 1817 boosted the lime trade on the Tamar. A kiln was put up at Tavistock after the canal

---

* In 1898 a tramp was found dead on top of a lime kiln at Cattedown, Plymouth, with one of his hands and part of his thighs and legs burnt away. He had gone to sleep on the lip of the kiln and was presumed to have become overcome by the fumes. (WDM 10 January 1898.)

was built, and another at Mill Hill to burn the lime carried over the canal's Mill Hill branch. In 1819, over 10,000 tons, or an average of over 800 tons a month, was carried over the canal and in the first ten years of its working nearly 70,000 tons of limestone was shipped through Morwellham, having been brought up the Tamar from Plymouth in barges[5].

The lime trade on the Tamar reached its height between the years 1810 and 1850; after that it began to decline with the use of artificial and chemical manures, the latter being readily available from the growing chemical industry in Plymouth.

Coal and carriage ruled the price of limestone and any increase in coal prices added 1d or $1\frac{1}{2}$d to the cost of a bushel of lime. The general rise in the cost of living through the middle and latter part of the last century raised the price of lime at places like Tavistock, Halton Quay and Cotehele Quay to 13s 6d a ton.

The two quays most closely identified with the lime trade in the Tamar Valley were Halton Quay and Newquay (see Chapter Two). From Halton Quay horse-drawn wagons supplied St Mellion and St Dominic, two districts which in the nineteenth century were increasingly given over to intensive market gardening. The four kilns at Halton were capable of turning out between 500 and 600 tons of burnt lump lime a year and could be pressed if necessary to 1,000 tons. This quay served an area not easily accessible from any railway system and its kilns had a longer active life than any others on the river. The last lime to be made in kilns by the Tamar was burnt here in 1916 for dressing Viverdon Down—then being ploughed up as a war measure[6]. They closed down a few months afterwards because of the cost and difficulty of getting coal from South Wales.

Newquay's kilns (whose remains are described on page 79) were reputed to be among the busiest on the river for they supplied lime for most of the rich farmland west of Tavistock. The memories of older people living in the district are not so much of the mines whose produce Newquay once shipped as of the days when farmers rose at four in the morning to be first in the queue for the lime which had been drawn long enough from the kilns to cool. The late ones were often left with stones almost too hot to touch, which charred and sometimes set fire to their carts. The concentration of farm carts and drivers jostling for position on the narrow approach road to New-quay led to such angry scenes that a check post was placed in the road at the top of the hill, and by an unwritten law whoever was first at this post was first served at the kilns.

The active life of the Newquay kilns ended in 1904 when the firm operating them transferred its business to Halton Quay. They were reopened by the Duke of Bedford for his tenants shortly before the first world war, but closed finally in 1914. Newquay's celebrated $1\frac{1}{2}$ cwt iron bushel measure with which the lime was measured out went to Halton Quay, remaining in use there until 1916. The New-quay lime-burner at the beginning of the century lived at Calstock, walking to and from his kilns each day, and when they closed he tended those at Halton—the last lime-burner to be actively em-ployed on the riverside kilns of the Tamar.

Between Hole's Hole and Gunnislake the remains of twenty or more lime kilns, all with their characteristic round arches, can be found today on both sides of the river bank. Some, such as the cluster at Pentillie (difficult to approach by land and best seen from the river) were set up and operated privately. The kilns at Cotehele (listed on page 81), supplied a large part of the Cotehele estate and the beautiful but little known Bohetherick Valley, where Walter Lowry started the Tamar Valley strawberry-growing industry. The kilns at Calstock (page 80) supplied farms around Kelly Bray and Stoke Climsland, while the area around Gunnislake drew its lime from three kilns on the river towpath below the village (page 80). All of them now have had their fires quenched for ever.

THE REMAINS OF THE TAMAR VALLEY KILNS

Lime kilns were usually built into a bank with an access path made to the top of the wells, the front and sides of these being protected by a thick wall. The entrance arches at either end of the kilns (or sometimes in front) enabled the burnt lime to be taken out and also gave access to the fire grate. A kiln was referred to as 'discharging' when lime was being drawn from it. Most of the smaller roadside kilns had two wells but the bigger ones on important quays had three or four. Some of the latter are often quite elaborately constructed with an inner communicating passage linking the wells.

The following list includes all the kilns seen and known to be associated with the lime trade in the Valley, although it is possible that isolated ones may have been missed. Many are now disappearing with road improvements.

Weir Quay

Two, some distance apart, on the road from Weir Quay to Clamoak. Both are old and probably each had two wells, but it is difficult today to see how they were approached.

Hole's Hole

On the river's edge. There is an approach from the road to Weir Quay, and two shallow depressions mark where the wells have been filled. Used as an Air Raid Precaution post in the last war. Each of these kilns is small and long disused.

South Hooe

Below the farm of that name and marked on the 6-in map. Probably had two wells, but long disused.

Rumleigh

Close to a disused quay below Rumleigh brickworks. Also marked on 6-in map.

Gawton

A remarkably fine and elaborately constructed group of three kilns, almost hidden by swampy undergrowth. Difficult to find and best approached from the path by Rumleigh Farm leading to Gawton Quay. Probably disused before the Newquay kilns higher up the river.

Newquay

The kilns lie hidden at the foot of a steep hill amid a tangle of ivy, birch and bramble. The loading bay and approach road can be made out through the undergrowth, and a flight of stone steps beside the kilns gives access to the three deep wells, one still partially covered by its iron grating, the other two dangerously open to the skies. The wells, 20 ft deep and 10 ft across, are cone-shaped and beautifully constructed. At least one appears to have its fire-door intact. A loading ramp in front of the kilns is still visible. An elaborately constructed group, with fanciful half-arches which suggest flying buttresses, and one of the few groups with the wells unfilled. A water-wheel worked incline was used to carry the stones from the barges.

Morwellham

Fine group by river's edge with stone loading bay still intact. Another, probably older, at rear of Ship Inn.

Tavistock

There was a kiln by the Tavistock Canal basin about 1830 to burn limestone carried over the canal. Rent was paid for a stream of water from the canal to work the 'limekiln machinery'. Its site is difficult to identify today.

Mill Hill

In a garden at the back of an old mill and storehouse, now known as the granary. It was put up in 1819, to burn lime carried over the Mill Hill 'cut' of the Tavistock Canal—one of the few whose construction can be precisely dated.

Gunnislake

Built into the bank below Gunnislake hill and best approached by the river path. Densely screened by swampy growth, they are difficult to find today, and the wells have been filled. Of massive, functional and bold construction, they are probably with the Calstock group the most imposing kilns on the river—like castles, as Gilpin observed.

Whimple

Once an important but now entirely forgotten lime-burning centre. There appear to have been four kilns here close to the river, standing either side of a rough track leading from Hatches Green. Very solid in appearance but now much overgrown and crumbling. There are ruins of cottages and a small quay nearby, part of a settlement deserted for nearly fifty years. Area once noted for its cherry gardens.

Calstock

Probably four kilns, the last of which, near the Danescombe Hotel, incorporates granite blocks in its masonry. Some of these kilns, all fronting the river, were much frequented by sailors, bargemen and quay workers for roasting potatoes for snacks.

Cotehele

The most picturesque in appearance and situation in the Tamar Valley, and incorporating a lime-burner's cottage. They have often been painted and sketched. There is a water colour in the British Museum of a kiln working at Cotehele.

Pentillie

The three privately constructed estate kilns here appear not to have been worked this century.

Halton Quay

Built against a ledge in the river bank. The wells are hewn out of rock and are about 20 ft deep and 10 ft across. An iron vent-pipe protruding out of the mud near the quay is said to have given added draught to the fire. The approach path for horses can be clearly made out, although a water-wheel working a small incline plane to haul up the stones to the lip of the kilns is said to have been used here in the last century. In their unusual construction (slate with limestone courses alternating), their siting and massive appearance probably the most interesting group on the river and worth preserving.

CHAPTER FIVE

The Pageantry of the Paddle Steamers

THE paddle steamer weaves a brightly coloured strand in the Tamar's history. The thump and clank of paddle wheels as steamers took people to market, pulled laden barges or took excursionists to see the Devon Rhine was the most familiar noise on the river in the last century. When the steam locomotive was little more than an inventor's plaything, the paddle steamer was bringing about a social and economic change in the lives and habits of people in the Tamar Valley far more complete than that achieved by the railway when Calstock was finally linked to a main-line system at Bere Alston nearly 100 years later. As the excursion habit grew in popularity in Victorian years, the paddle steamer added a new meaning and dimension to the use of leisure, and brought to the river and the little settlements bordering it a rich pattern of incident and pageantry which many people still remember with nostalgia.

EARLY RIVER TRAVEL

Movement away from the river has always been difficult in the Tamar Valley, as mentioned in Chapter Two. As late as 1856, J. Allen in his *History of Liskeard* complained that there was more difficulty in performing the 20 miles from Plymouth to Liskeard than the 246 miles between Plymouth and London and the expense was almost equal. Before a paddle-steamer service was established, people living in Callington, Gunnislake, Calstock and even Tavistock, rather than face the roundabout road journey to visit the markets of Plymouth and Devonport, congregated at Calstock be-

tween one and two in the morning and waited before a huge log fire
to be rowed down the river on the early-morning tide. Others would
be picked up at Morwellham and Cotehele. It was not uncommon
for them to be overtaken by dense fog at Halton Quay, the six-oared
boat and its shivering passengers and crew being marooned for
several hours.

It was much the same story for people wanting to travel up the
river. When the Rev William Gilpin towards the end of the eighteenth century was touring the Western Counties he heard much
about the scenery of the Tamar Valley; but the only way he could
see it was by being rowed up the river by 'four stout hands of the
Ocean man o' war'. Others, less privileged, had to bargain with the
watermen who thronged the estuary.

The first paddle-steamer service on the Tamar seems to have
been established in 1820 or 1821, nearly twenty years after the first
practical paddle steamer had been demonstrated in Scotland, and
Richard Trevithick had proved at Beacon Hill, Camborne, that his
steam carriage could successfully haul loads over a prepared track.
This early service on the Tamar seems, according to Rowe's
Panorama of Plymouth, to have been primarily a market boat running between Calstock and Devonport: by this time the Tamar
Valley was firmly established as the market garden of Plymouth.
From the rich farm lands around Launceston alone came 30,000
tons of pork, poultry, butter and eggs a year. H. E. Carrington
declared that Devonport Market was widely recognized as the
cheapest in the kingdom for provisions[1].

FIRST STEAMER EXCURSIONS

Much of this traffic was waterborne, either in barges down the
Tamar itself or ferried across the river from Saltash. The early
steamer excursions on the Tamar stemmed from the establishment

in 1823-5 of a regular steam-packet service between Plymouth, Portsmouth and Falmouth. The Plymouth, Devonport & Falmouth Steam Packet Company's first vessel, the 170-ton paddle steamer *Sir Francis Drake*, was completed at Cattedown in the summer of 1823[2]. The *Drake* was advertised as being 'open for engagement by private parties' who were 'urged to book a week in advance'[3]. In between regular runs to Falmouth she made excursions to Cotehele and Calstock 'on which occasions the company are enlivened by a military band'. By 1825 she had been joined by the 250-ton paddle steamer *Brunswick*. Although vessels of 300 tons could navigate then as far as Morwellham, the *Brunswick* seems not to have been used on the Tamar, her excursions being mostly out to the Eddystone and back.

By the late 1840s a fleet of small paddle steamers of 'easy draught', among them the *Alert*, *Phoenix*, *Queen* and *Empress*, were employed on regular passenger and excursion services on the Tamar, and with their ample deck space, refreshment saloon, and some shelter from wet weather, they were not despised by even the wealthier people of the neighbourhood.

The new method of travel was not without its hazards. The boiler of the *Queen* steamer blew up on the Tamar in July 1850[4], killing one man (the *Queen* was an unlucky steamer—she was rammed by a tug in 1864 and scrapped shortly afterwards); while the number of drowning fatalities arising from the increasing use of the river began to cause alarm as early as 1831, when a Plymouth & Tamar Humane Society was formed[5]. Rewards were offered to rescuers and life-saving apparatus deposited at convenient points. The wash from the steamers also overturned small boats, eroded the river bank and during high tides knocked people off the quays.

Although the railway had reached Plymouth in 1849 it made little difference to the fleet of steamers, which were not seriously challenged until the arrival of the motor-coach after the first world war. The well-planned rail excursions of Thomas Cook, a feature of the

British scene from 1840 onwards, were impracticable in an area like the Tamar Valley.

Indeed, at weekends the steamers began to compete with the churches, and this drew a weighty 'remonstrance' from the senior clergy of Plymouth on the evils of pleasure trips on Sundays[6]. On weekdays when the tides were right, anything up to a thousand people would descend on Calstock during a day, and the large banqueting hall at Cotehele had to be pressed into use as a dining-room. Not all the trips were from Plymouth—for instance, in September 1856 over 200 people 'connected with the Gunnislake Wesleyan Chapel' made a river excursion to Plymouth.

The success of the Tamar trips prompted excursion parties to explore the adjoining Yealm and Lynher rivers. On 19 August 1850 the *Empress* made the first recorded steamer trip up the river Yealm 'to the wonder of the inhabitants who hastened from all points to behold the paddling leviathan on the quiet and mirrory expanse of the river, the smoke curling up to the azure vault of the sky'[7].

THE FIRST STEAMERS

The steamers making these journeys were crude by later standards. They were about 70 ft long, 'furnished with high pressure boilers', and are described as being capable of about 12 or 15 knots. Some were constructed locally, for in 1856 Messrs Milstead Anthony of Plymouth, who had a busy foundry which made a number of mine pumping-engines, were building two iron steamers of these dimensions for carrying 'passengers to the different landing places of the three towns'[8]. Besides the four steamers earlier mentioned there was the *Albatross*, which also made regular trips to Malpass (for Truro), and the steamer *Gipsy*.

The last named was one of three steamers owned by the Saltash & St Germans Steamboat Co., which had been established in 1854

F

by a group of 'gentlemen, farmers and residents in Devonport, Saltash and neighbouring towns with a view to accommodating themselves and the public'[9]. In the autumn of 1856 a rival concern appeared, the Saltash Watermen's Steam Packet Co., which announced that the 'rapid increase of persons travelling between Saltash and Devonport in the last two years induced by the beauty of the Hamoaze and the rapid progress of the Royal Albert Bridge had given rise to the feeling that another line of small steamers may be advantageously put on'[10]. Undertaking to provide two 'good and safe boats adapted to the requirements of the passenger traffic of the neighbourhood' it announced the purchase of the *Albert* steamer, capacity 200 persons, which made frequent excursions up the Tamar.

The older company, through a series of press advertisements, implied that the Watermen's company was financially unsound and that 'Our own steamers do not always pay their way or even defray the cost of their coals.'

THE EXCURSION HABIT

This may have been true during the winter but the summer demand expanded yearly to stretch the resources of all available steamers. In fifty years from 1801 the combined population of Plymouth, Stonehouse and Devonport had grown, to reach over 103,000, and the growth of mining had doubled and trebled the population of the Valley itself. The Victorian picnic and excursion habit was at its height, and steamers for river trips were being chartered long in advance much as coaches are today. Every religious, philanthropic and social organization in the district regarded its activities as incomplete without at least one steamer trip to Weir Head or Calstock.

Then, in the summer of 1856 a long-talked-of event set the seal of royal patronage on the Tamar and its steamers. This was the visit of Queen Victoria, the Prince Consort and the royal children to Endsleigh, the Duke of Bedford's seat. The journey was made by steamer as far as Morwellham, the royal party disembarking there to be taken to Endsleigh by coach. For part of the river trip the Queen and her party travelled in the little steamer *Gipsy* probably quite unaware that eight months earlier the *Gipsy* had been sunk at her moorings at Saltash 'because one of the pipes connecting with the machinery having been carelessly left open water was admitted to the hold of the vessel'.

The visit was a great success and boat owners and others were not slow to take advantage of the prestige bestowed on the 'expeditious method of water conveyance'. To remedy Calstock's complete lack of amenities for entertaining visitors, the Ashburton Hotel was completed in 1859. It was soon advertising 'water boiled and tea made for parties'. And serious efforts were now made to publicize the Tamar trips. In July 1860 the *Plymouth Mail* began to carry advertisements for the 'fast and commodious steamer Princess' then undertaking trips to Weir Head for 1s 6d return, a price which included the attendance of a quadrille band. More varied and interesting were the excursions advertised at the same time in the steamer *Fairy*, for they provide one of the earliest examples of railway co-operation. Throughout the summer of 1860 the *Fairy* made regular trips to 'Mr. Jackson's tea and fruit gardens at Beerferris', the South Devon Railway providing special 4d tickets from Plymouth to Devonport and Saltash to be used on trains which linked with the steamers. At the gardens 'tea, fruit, cream, hot water and every kind of refreshment and accommodation could be had' as well as a large marquee for dancing.

Early in the 1860s there arrived 'Mr Rowe', a tireless and skilful practitioner in regular newspaper advertising. Rowe did not own any steamers but set himself up as an agent for those who did—an early example of a public relations officer. It was he, in the summer of 1863, who started the first regular cheap trips on the river. Continually 'Rowe's pleasant trips' were advertised in Plymouth's two daily papers[11]. The competition he stimulated brought down the return fare for a steamer trip to Calstock from 1s 6d to 1s. When the Saturday half-holiday movement was inaugurated in the following year, Rowe's special August trip to Weir Head to celebrate the occasion was 'rewarded by a numerous party who were greatly entertained not only by the beauties of the scenery but by the music of some members of the South Devon Militia band . . . which was more agreeable than that usually provided for such occasions'.

New steamers appeared, of course, among them *Wellington, Contractor* and *Volunteer*, the first-named, along with the *Princess*, being owned by the Devon & Cornwall Steam Packet Co. Rowe skilfully studied his public. Ordinary trips were kept strictly to 1s, but a steamer to Weir Head could be hired for 'more select parties' at 1s 6d to 2s a head, and for these a 'superior quadrille band' was provided. Organizations chartering the 'powerful steamer *Emperor*' could have the benefit of the Royal Marine Band. More spectacular were the occasions when fleets of five steamers would transport a thousand people for a day's outing to Calstock. This was the way officers and men of the 2nd Queen's Own went up the river with their commanding officer in the first week of August 1864, the time at Calstock being spent in playing quoits, cricket, football and listening to the regimental band. At intervals throughout the summer other regiments from the garrison made similar trips, 'spacious rooms being engaged at Calstock to feed the troops'.

SANITARY CONDITIONS

Weir Head, just below Gunnislake, afforded the river tourists some of the most spectacular scenery in the Tamar Valley, comparatively unspoiled by human habitation. There were no liquor houses nearby and the excursion parties were comparatively orderly But at Calstock, 4 miles downstream, things were different. Here there were people who viewed with mixed feelings the 'living freights' which a succession of steamers deposited on the quays. The town had no policeman and no amenities; many of the trippers thronged the beer houses and became caught up in drunken brawls. A drunk and disorderly crowd from three steamers on one Sunday in April 1854 aroused so much uproar that in a chapel 'situated near the scene of the commotion the voice of the officiating minister could with difficulty be heard'[12]. Another resident, who found the 'habitual practice of drunkeness in Calstock disgusting' encountered six intoxicated persons while walking between Gunnislake and Calstock all of whom swore disgustingly when civilly accosted.

This drunkenness went hand in hand with a complete lack of sanitation. In the summer Calstock could be smelt from a distance. There were no covered sewers, two-thirds of the dwellings which inadequately housed a population of over 2,500 were without water closets, and the streets were left ankle-deep in filth. The General Board of Health sent a medical officer to look into the 'sanitary state of Calstock' and in May 1854 he produced a scarifying report disclosing 'a picture of filthiness such as could scarcely be equalled in the rude hamlets of savage life'[13]. Refuse from middens and pigsties was left heaped against houses, the undrained refuse of three slaughter-houses 'added to the pestiferous vapours which such filth must engender', while the water supply consisted of one spring and an old mine adit. There was no public lighting, no cleansing authority and in wet weather the streets were covered from end to end in inches of mud.

After reading the report the parish overseers, largely landlords and farmers, sent a 'courteous acknowledgment' and complained privately that their tenants were too poor to have rents raised to effect improvements. For another dozen years Calstock wallowed in its filth, amid increasing outcries from more enlightened residents.

But Victorian travellers were unfussy if not always long-lived. Many parts of Plymouth and Devonport were little better than Calstock in 1864, and the observation of the investigator of Calstock's 'sanitary state' that 'parties of pleasure now ascending the Tamar are deterred from visiting Calstock a second time because there is no favourable accommodation and the streets are filthy' proved wide of the mark. On one day in July 1865 the *Ariel* had to leave so many behind from an advertised excursion to Weir Head that the *Gipsy* was called in to take the overflow.

THE CONFIDENT YEARS

The 60s gave way to the 70s, and the golden age of steamer travel was settled on the broad and winding river, which was enjoying a heyday to last until the first world war. The river captains became a favoured and envied élite and the opportunity to command a river steamer a much sought-after honour; when Captain Whitburn was appointed to the *Ariel* in 1878 he went before the full board of the Tamar & Tavy Steamship Co., which carefully scrutinized not only his professional qualifications but his background. The captains were strong personalities in their own right and not infrequently their care and attention brought them rewards from contented passengers.

The lack of a landing point to serve the Hoe was partly remedied in the early 1880s by the building of West Hoe Pier and basin at Plymouth, and Rowe was advertising trips from there in the *Eleanor* and *Princess* by 1882. Then in May of that year the Plymouth Promenade Pier was opened for steamers, and under the management of James McBryde it became a favourite point of departure. McBryde rivalled Rowe in forceful and energetic advertising, offering excursions to Calstock and Weir Head in the *Ariel, Albert, Empress* and *Eleanor*, some of them starting as early as 8.30 in the morning. The steamers for these trips were advertised as being constructed

especially for passenger traffic and are only so used. Each steamer carries a stewardess and assistants and tea and light refreshments are served on board as well as fruit in season. Where so much is of interest on the tours it is not easy to indicate the exact position of each particular object but the Captains and crews of the Steamer are able and will be found willing to give the necessary information.

By this time Calstock had also been cleaned up, drains connected to the houses, sewers laid 'with the new glazed pipes', the water supply improved and a constable installed. Desire to retain the lucrative steamer traffic undoubtedly expedited the sanitary measures. The town's reputation as a pest house duly gave way to fame of a sweeter kind founded on its local strawberry beds. The lush, ripe fruit left over after the demands of Covent Garden had been satisfied was offered with liberal helpings of Cornish cream as a tempting bait for day trippers, the sales proving a lucrative sideline for housewives. Tiny riverside cottage parlours were turned into tea rooms, and as the laden steamers drew alongside white-aproned women greeted them and sold punnets of fruit at 2d, along with nosegays of cottage flowers. Farther along the quay, donkeys could be hired for 1s a time for jaunts along woodland and riverside paths. In spite of the recurrent financial crises of the 1860s, prices remained remarkably stable. In the 1870s the return trip to Calstock still cost only 1s 3d, and passengers who used the market boat could take up to 2 cwt of merchandise for 6d.

LATER STEAMERS

As the expansive and confident later years of Victoria's reign unfolded, people were demanding more comfort, and ship design was becoming more sophisticated. These trends were reflected in the steamer *Ariel*, whose design, appearance and fittings ushered in a new standard for the Tamar. Built on the Clyde, she was licensed to carry 150 passengers but, as *The Western Morning News* of 5 June 1865 noted, 'she is capable of carrying a much larger number if stowed in the manner usually adopted in these vessels'. The *Ariel* was 112 ft long (the longest by far of any steamer on the Tamar up till then) and drew only 2 ft 7 in of water. She first appeared on the river in the summer of 1865, being in breath-taking contrast to the crude and dilapidated steamers she supplanted. For about a third of her length she had 'two spacious saloons 7 ft high handsomely fitted up for accommodation of passengers'. Lockers throughout the length of these saloons were upholstered with horsehair cushions covered in plush velvet, while mahogany tables ran down the centre. Room was provided for a piano, and there was apparatus for the preparation of tea and coffee. Even more revolutionary for the time was the toilet accommodation: separate lavatories were provided for men and women, it was proudly announced. The point was worth making, for the earlier steamers frequently had none at all.

With her long glass-topped saloon flashing in the sun, *Ariel* was affectionately known as the 'glass house' and rhymes were made up to celebrate her prowess and superiority. Her career lasted well into the 1890s, but her supremacy became increasingly challenged by the new steamers coming to the river in the late 1870s. The *Eleanor* filched from her the title of the most graceful steamer on the river, her smoothness and speed making her a favourite for church excursions and outings. In a little under three years (1880) the *Empress* appeared—the outcome, it is said, of a wager to build a faster and bigger boat than *Ariel*. The *Empress* was bigger but it was at the cost of speed; in fact she achieved renown up and down the Tamar as the 'market boat', running a regular service three times a week between Calstock and Devonport. In 1888 came the pride of the Saltash Steamboat Co's fleet, the handsome, large and powerful *Alexandra*, for long the fastest steamer on the river. A companion vessel to her was the *Princess Royal*, built at Plymouth and launched in March 1888 (see pages 95–100 for more details of these).

But times were changing and becoming more competitive. In 1891 the old Saltash Steamboat Co. was re-formed as the Saltash Three Towns & District Steamboat Co., taking over a small ferry-boat service which had been started by John Parsons to run between Devonport and Millbrook, a hamlet on a tidal creek opposite Devonport where many naval men and dockyard workers lived. After a few years of uneasy partnership Parsons broke away from the company and started in opposition a fleet of paddle steamers of his own. Into the busy traffic on the Tamar he introduced three notable vessels— the *Brunel*, *Hibernia* and *Britannia*, all built in the Edwardian era and still remembered with affection by many people. With these and other vessels, Parsons, who by now had formed a company of his own, the Millbrook Steamboat Co., declared war on his Saltash rivals; and the last years of the paddle-steamer age on the Tamar were enlivened by a fierce rivalry and enmity which split people into factions and led to a number of lawsuits.

Parsons's steamers had red funnels; the Saltash Co's were painted buff. In speed and manœuvrability Parsons's boats were generally considered to have a slight edge, but both firms had a noisy army of staunch supporters who waged a 'red' and 'white' funnel war which reverberated throughout the valley. Rival captains raced each other up and down the river to gain vantage-points at landing places; passengers placed wagers on the result. The competition became most bitter at the ferry crossings between Millbrook and Devonport, where both companies used the same piers. Steamer captains ruthlessly tried to jockey their rivals on to the mud, sometimes leaving the hapless passengers stranded until the incoming tide refloated them. Collisions brought about by deliberate 'bumping' and 'boring' became almost commonplace. Between January 1895 and February 1899, Parsons brought sixteen successful claims for damages against the Saltash Company, the County Court judge making wry asides about the competition between 'spirited companies'.

DECLINE AND RECOVERY

With the dawn of the new century, although competition still brought unexpected excitement to many trips, the rivals gradually settled down to share the river traffic between them. It was not negligible. Through the years of the Victorian and Edwardian peace as many as 100,000 people a year patronized the river and sea trips[14]. On the now-deserted stretch of river between Calstock and Weir Head the rival *Alexandra* and *Brunel* would pass each other abreast, their combined bulk almost filling the width of the river. The channel was less silted then, due to the constant traffic and to the fact that many steamers trailed a chain astern to keep the river bed scoured. Because of their size the *Alexandra* and *Brunel* were warped round with ropes at Weir Head, a performance always watched by a crowd. The smaller steamers did it on their engines, but it was an operation not without hazard, the son of Captain Whitburn of the *Empress* being drowned after falling overboard when the steamer was making its turn. The grief-stricken father afterwards emigrated to New Zealand.

Until 1914 the fare to Weir Head and back—a round trip of almost 40 miles—still cost only 1s 9d. For value, comfort and enjoyment there were still no other tours in the neighbourhood to match the steamer excursions. The Great Western Railway's chief attraction was a clumsy combined rail and coach tour to Two Bridges and Princetown costing 4s 9d, or one could go by the twenty-six-seater Albion motor-coaches to Seaton and Downderry. The South Western made an impression on the commercial traffic, but its effect on the pleasure trips was negligible. There was dancing at Weir Head and on the quay at Morwellham, while Morwell Rocks were full of picnic parties. During the long summer days of 1914 the river pageantry was at its brightest and gayest. Few realized that the echoing bugle calls which ushered in August 1914 sounded also the swan-song of the paddle-steamer age on the Tamar. While the papers were full of stories of German guns bombarding Namur and of British troops retreating from Mons, the *Alexandra*, *Princess Royal* and *Eleanor*, along with the *Brunel* and *Hibernia*, continued making their stately progress to Weir Head. But after 1914 it was never to be the same. One by one in the succeeding years the steamers were called away to sterner duties. Among the first to go was the handsome *Brunel*, sent out to Mesopotamia from where she never returned. The *Hibernia* went in 1916 to Scapa Flow, and the *Alexandra* in 1917 to Rosyth, returning so much the worse for wear that daylight could be seen through the rust holes in her funnel.

For a brief period in the 1920s the pageant was renewed. The *Empress* took up the three-day-a-week market run between Calstock and Devonport and for two or three seasons, particularly during the long summer of 1921, the landing piers were as thronged as before the war. But the motor-coach and car were now appearing as strong competitors. One by one the ageing steamers were replaced by handier motor-launches. The last survivor of the steam age on the Tamar was the *Empress*. Her departure for scrapping in the early 1930s paved the way for the diesel age, ushered in in 1935 by the *Devon Belle*[15]. Her diesel successors today when the weather and tides allow still make the trips to Calstock and Weir Head, carrying in a good season about 2,000 passengers—a far cry from the 1,000 a day who a century ago visited Calstock in the 'powerful' steamer *Emperor* or the 'commodious' *Volunteer*.

DETAILS OF THE STEAMERS

The details below cover most of the better-known paddle steamers on the river between 1865 and 1914. A number of others were almost exclusively used on the ferry services between Devonport, Millbrook and Cremyll and between Plymouth and Oreston, and though they have a fascinating story in their own right they are outside the scope of this work.

Ariel

Iron paddle steamer. Hull by Hedderwick of Govan, engines by A. J. Bennie. Length 120 ft, beam 14 ft, depth 7 ft. Tubular boiler with 'engines of almost 30 h.p. on the oscillating principle', 10 knots. Paddles worked 'with patent feather floats'. She was sailed round from the Clyde to Plymouth when completed in 1865, extra coal being stacked in the saloon for the journey which took four days. The end of the *Ariel* is uncertain. She ran aground and sank on a sandbank just below Calstock but was salvaged and repaired; probably she was scrapped in the early 1900s after more than forty years' service. She was possibly the best-loved boat on the river, many of her fittings being bought as souvenirs by sentimental travellers when she was broken up.

Iolanthe and Lady of the Lake

Twin-screw steamers whose date of construction is unknown. Much employed on ferry duties between Devonport and Saltash but did occasional excursion trips, the *Lady of the Lake* often being seen at Lopwell on the Tavy. Both reputed to be painfully slow and were probably scrapped in the early part of the century.

Eleanor

Iron paddle steamer. Built in the late 1870s by Willoughby's of Plymouth. About 10 knots. She replaced an earlier *Elénore* said to have been built in France for service on the Seine. In appearance one of the most graceful and smooth-running boats on the Tamar and a favourite for church outings. One of the first steamers to resume excursion trips after the 1914 war. Scrapped about 1930.

Empress

Iron paddle steamer. 101 tons. Hull and engines built about 1880 by W. Allsupp, Preston, Lancs. Length 115 ft, beam 16 ft 2 in, depth 4 ft 9 in. Cylinders 30-in stroke. Reboilered 1889 and 1908. Employed as the market boat, running between Calstock and North Corner three times a week. Her funnel had a distinctive black top with a metal ring below. Converted into a house boat, ending her days on the river Yealm.

Princess Royal

Steel paddle steamer. 105 tons. Length 124 ft, beam 16½ ft, depth 4 ft 7 in. Oscillating engine. Cylinders 19 in and 32 in, stroke 30 in. 11 knots on trials. Built by Willoughby's, launched 29 March 1888. Larger and improved *Eleanor* and as first built had a low bow and stern. Given a flush deck fore and aft in 1891 for excursion work in the Channel, provided with solid gunwales instead of open rails, had funnel raised and fitted with two pole masts. Often made cruises to Salcombe, Torquay, Looe and Fowey. Scrapped 1927.

Alexandra

Steel paddle steamer. 127 tons. Built and engined by Allsup, Preston, 1888. In service August of that year. Length 135 ft, beam 17 ft 3 in, depth 8 ft 3 in. Cylinders 20 in and 38 in, stroke 36 in. 11 knots. The pride of the company's fleet and its largest boat. Shared many of the longer sea excursion duties with the *Princess Royal*. Reboilered 1902. On return from war service largely rebuilt by Rogers of Cremyll and put into service again on August Bank Holiday 1920. Her paddles broke during a trip up the river Yealm. Scrapped 1927.

Lady Ernestine

Paddle steamer. Built Willoughby's. Oscillating engines. Mainly

seen on the ferry run between Millbrook, Mutton Cove and Devonport. Her shallow draught made her difficult to handle at low tide.
Only steamer in the company's fleet to have paddles aft of the
funnel. Lay unused at Saltash during the 1914 war and disappeared
immediately afterwards.

Prince Edward

Paddle steamer. Built at Dartmouth 1904 by Philip & Son. Larger
than the *Lady Ernestine* and much used for trips to Cawsand. Had
a comparatively short life, being scrapped in the early 1920s.

Victoria, Albert and Princess

Although often used on excursion trips (when always advertised
as steamers and not 'saloon' steamers) were really tugs. *Victoria*
(built 1881, screw, 40 tons, length 77 ft, beam 13 ft 1 in, depth
6 ft 9 in, 25 h.p.) was for many years a duty tug at Calstock. *Albert*
(1882, screw, 61 tons, length 84 ft, beam 14 ft, depth 8 ft 5 in,
22 h.p.) and *Princess* (1888, screw, 45 tons, length 78 ft, beam
13 ft 4 in, depth 7 ft, 18 h.p.) were both built by Willoughby's.
Drawing more water than paddle steamers they frequently ran out
into the Channel. Were a familiar sight on the river towing coal
barges. All were scrapped in the 1920s.

All the above were owned by the company which after 1891
became the Saltash Three Towns & District Steamboat Co. Ltd. It
was absorbed in the 1920s by its rival, the Millbrook Steamboat Co.

The Saltash Company's vessels had the following livery: black
hulls with green water line; pale-blue cabins; buff funnels with
black tops; black-sided paddle boxes with yellow tops; cabin line
marked in blue along the side.

Cornubia

Paddle steamer, built probably in the early 1890s by Waterman
of Cremyll. Driven by two compound condensing engines. A fast

and shapely boat distinguished by a very tall upright funnel—all the other steamers had a slight rake in their funnels. Taken over by the Admiralty early in the 1914 war and never returned.

Devonia

Built at Cremyll about 1895, where her hull was fitted with engines by Plenty Bros of Newbury. Had a fore cabin and was built in forward to go outside the breakwater to Cawsand and the Yealm estuary. The boat was frequently seen to be shaking because of the vibrations set up by her engines, and her generally ungainly appearance earned her the name of 'The Junk'. Scrapped at Stonehouse 1915–16.

Britannia

Paddle steamer. Built and engined in 1900 by Philip of Dartmouth. Length 80 ft, beam 16 ft, depth 7 ft 6 in. Cylinders 11 in and 22 in; stroke 24 in. Boiler 7 ft × 7 ft 6 in. Had six floats to her paddles instead of the usual eight, which gave her a distinctive 'flap, flap, flap' sound. Scrapped in the 1930s.

Hibernia

Paddle steamer. Built and engined 1903 by Philip. Length 110 ft, beam 16 ft, depth 8 ft 3 in. Cylinders $12\frac{1}{2}$ in and 25 in; stroke 26 in, boiler 8 ft 6 in × 8 ft 6 in. 11 to 12 knots. Larger and more powerful than *Britannia*; paddles aft of funnel which was very large and upright. Carried 366 passengers and was the first boat on the river to have electric light. Was specifically built for river trips and her boilers required 15 tons of coal a week. Was also notable for having steam-controlled steering and a tea as well as a beer bar. Broken up in the early 1930s.

Brunel

Paddle steamer. Built 1905 for a London County Council steamer service on the Thames which failed to pay its way. Said to have cost over £3,000, and bought for between £250 and £300 by Parsons. First appeared in Plymouth in 1909 and defied convention by making her maiden trip up the river on Friday, 13 August of that year, the initials LCC still plainly discernible on her paddle boxes. Slightly larger than the *Princess Royal* and fitted with forced draught, she was at 16 knots not only the largest but the fastest boat on the river, burning 20 tons of coal a week. Acquired by the Admiralty soon after the outbreak of war, she was adapted as a hospital ship and went out under her own steam to Mesopotamia, serving on the Tigris and Euphrates. She never returned.

The last five steamers were owned by the Millbrook Steamboat Co which exists now as the Millbrook Steamboat & Trading Co, with offices at Cremyll, and runs the present-day river trips. Its steamers wore the following livery: black hulls with red and green water line; pale-blue cabins; red funnels with black tops; black paddle boxes with yellow stripes; cabin line marked in blue along the hull.

The 300-ton three-masted Tamar schooner Eleanor *and a 200-ton ketch alongside her at Goss's shipyard*

Ruins on the site of Gawton Quay. The leaning stack on the left marks the end of the arsenic flue from Gawton mine

I02

All that remains of the old Phoenix Brick & Tile works near Sevenstones. Bricks made here in the 1870s were exported to Russia

Discarded mouldings and ornamental terra-cotta tiles on the site of the old Tamar Firebrick & Tile works on Hingston Down

CHAPTER SIX

The Tavistock Canal

IN 1798 a nineteen-year-old engineer came to Tavistock to manage the Wheal Friendship copper mine at Mary Tavy. His salary was £100 a year, which he regarded as an 'uncommonly handsome allowance'; in thanking his employers he hoped that his services to them 'might be of the value they ought to expect'.

This young man was John Taylor. Born in Norfolk and trained as a land surveyor and civil engineer, he became in the next fifty years a leading figure in metalliferous mining, and left behind him in Tavistock an enduring memorial—the Tavistock Canal. (He also founded the firm of John Taylor & Son, which still has offices in London.)

Few things today are more evocative of the ambitions and energies of the early nineteenth-century leaders of industrial enterprise than this 4½-mile waterway which connected the Tavy to the Tamar. For nearly 2 miles it runs deep in a tunnel under Morwell Down. An incline plane with a remarkable drop of 237 ft connected it to Morwellham, and over its waters briskly moved what were probably the first iron barges to be seen on any English canal. It is still indirectly useful, providing the water power for a hydro-electric station on one of the quays at Morwellham to which it once brought the copper ore mined along its banks (see Chapter Seven).

The dilapidated square by which Tavistock commemorates Taylor's name is a poor tribute to a remarkable and many-sided man. In an age not over-scrupulous about working conditions, Taylor took as much care of his miners as he did of his employers' property, and when he left Tavistock in 1812, after only twelve years, during which he lived at nearby Holwell, they lined the

G   103

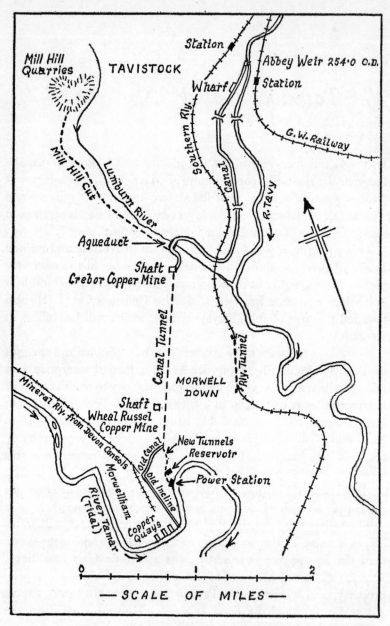

Tavistock Canal and the Mill Hill 'Cut' in relation to Morwellham streets in their work-stained clothes to demonstrate their affection for him. By the time he was twenty-one he had so organized and improved the Wheal Friendship mine near Mary Tavy that it had become one of the richest copper producers in the neighbourhood, and his ingenuity in harnessing the water power of the Tavy to work it foreshadowed in many ways the manner in which the Tamar, forty-five years later, was made to work Devon Great Consols mine. At one time or another he had a close interest in all the principal mines of the area, and he is a key figure in its early industrial development.

Tavistock, 1840

~~Mr.~~ *Wheal Friendship Mine Acco.*

To GILL, RUNDLE, AND Co,
MORWELLHAM.

To Canal ... Bridge
Works Quarter 10/0 ... 133-15 0

His energy and curiosity overflowed in many outside interests. He wrote an invaluable and highly characteristic introduction to the 1811 edition of Risdon's *Survey of Devonshire*. He helped found the Tavistock library, became one of the earliest members of the Geological Society, and was a founder-member of the British Association and one of its most prolific correspondents. The German explorer Humboldt, famous for his discoveries in South America, was his friend, and he was one of the first to advocate a mining school—a proposal later realized in the Camborne School of Mines.

THE NEED FOR TRANSPORT

When Taylor came to Tavistock there was virtually no wheeled transport in the area nor any roads fit to take it. Mineral ores, coal, manure, slate and lime had to be carried to and from Morwellham by packhorses over a network of steep pot-holed tracks which the autumn and winter rains turned into watercourses. These tracks were beaten out by the hooves of horse and mule teams in trains of thirty or fifty which were driven and tended, frequently with great cruelty, by teamsters whose staple diet was barley bread, skimmed milk and potatoes. Sand, manure, corn and lime were carried in bushel bags slung across the pack saddles, while stone, coal and mineral ores were transported in containers called 'pots' which had hinged bottoms for emptying[1].

The slowness and costliness of this transport—1s 6d a mile to carry $2\frac{1}{2}$ cwt—and the increasing output from the mines around Tavistock made it essential to find a cheaper and quicker means of carriage to the Tamar. Wheal Friendship was raising increasing quantities of ore each year while little more than a mile away Wheal Crowndale, rediscovered in 1799, had its sett choked with rich piles of copper ore. Taylor had a financial interest in this mine which had its water-wheels driven by a leat cut from the Tavy at Tavistock[2].

The leat may well have been the forerunner of the canal, for by 1800 the idea of linking the Tavy and the Tamar by a waterway had sufficiently crystallized in Taylor's mind for preliminary sketches to be prepared. At this time there were nearly 1,800 miles of canals in England; the Dudley Canal had a $1\frac{1}{4}$-mile tunnel largely pierced through limestone, and was one of the few precedents to which Taylor could refer in planning to bore through a hill of slate and hard elvan rock. He studied particularly the writings of John Smeaton, who had completed the Eddystone lighthouse in 1795 and was the foremost civil engineer of the day. The canal venture was also a mining speculation; Taylor elaborated on its objects as being to provide a navigation, to discover and drain copper and tin lodes, and to provide sufficient power 'to work engines of great magnitude' so as to render the canal's banks 'one of the most eligible situations in England for manufacturers requiring extensive powers of machinery'. He had demonstrated that it could reduce the cost of liming an acre of land from 15s to 5s, and the scheme was enthusiastically received in Tavistock.

In 1802 a survey had shown that a 4½-mile canal beginning from a weir near the Abbey Bridge, Tavistock, could be built for £40,000, a cost which included cutting the 1½-mile tunnel through Morwell Down and constructing a branch to the Mill Hill slate quarries north of Tavistock. The open waterway, budgeted for at 2s 6d a linear yard, was to be 16 ft wide and 3 ft deep. The tunnel, 7,920 ft long, was to be 8 ft high and 6 ft wide, with 3 ft of water. At its deepest point it would be 360 ft under Morwell Down. To provide current, the canal was to drop 4 ft, or roughly 1 ft a mile. In the event, the survey and alignment proved astonishingly accurate; the major miscalculation was in underestimating the hardness of the rock under the Down. This was to delay completion and add nearly £20,000 to the cost.

All the land needed was offered free by the Duke of Bedford, who in addition to dues for the use of quays at Morwellham was to receive a royalty of one-tenth on all ores mined. An Act obtained in 1803 authorized the capital of £40,000, to be subscribed in 400 shares of £100 each. Most of the money was found in Tavistock: the Duke himself took fifty shares, William Rundle, the banker and MP for Tavistock, took twenty-five, and another fifty were taken by the Birmingham Mining & Copper Company with which Taylor was connected.

CONSTRUCTION

Fourteen years of continuous labour started on 29 August 1803. The tunnel's course was marked out over Morwell Down by a line of white posts, shafts were sunk along the line and drives made to connect[3]. Black powder, emitting sulphurous smoke and fumes which made the labourers retch and choke, was used for blasting; otherwise the hard rock was split with steel wedges and hand borers which had steel bits fitted to iron shanks. These often broke off, and can still be seen embedded in the tunnel wall. The yearly reports of the committee of management supervising the work provide a vivid and arresting narrative of the hard struggle to build the canal, but they offer no evidence for the persistent and picturesque legend that it was done by French prisoners of war[4].

At the Tavistock end, work on the tunnel began by sinking a shaft near Crebor farm and making a cutting from it to the beginning of the aqueduct over the Lumburn Valley. A stream (which still flows) a few yards from the tunnel was turned into the cutting, enabling boats to take away rubble from the shaft and cutting to form the embankment for the aqueduct. There 'by a simple incline they were drawn out of the water upon an elevated railroad and made to discharge their load in a situation proper to the formation of the embankment'.

Quarries to provide stone for masonry work were opened on the spot (notably at the Fitzford slate outcrop), and after twelve months (by August 1804) some 52 fathoms of the tunnel had been driven, and the three main driving shafts and the two air shafts which marked its course were well advanced. (This rate of 372 ft a year in relatively easy ground may be compared with the 45 ft a week by which the tunnel for the new Victoria underground line is, in the 1960s, being driven through the stiff London clay.) The first year's working also brought early confirmation of copper lodes in the area, three bodies of ore varying from 3 to 12 ft in thickness being found a few fathoms in from the tunnel's northern portal. Plans were made to develop the find as Wheal Crebor—the name being that of the nearby farm and going back to Domesday—and from this time on the mining enterprise associated with the canal assumes a separate identity (see next chapter).

The approaches to the tunnel, whose levels had been contracted for at £7 a fathom, had been in comparatively soft ground, but as the cutting went deeper into the hill, hard elvan courses began to appear. The cost of excavating levels rose to £10 a fathom, but even more troublesome was 'bad air in the ends and water in the shafts'. The smoke from the shot blasts filled the narrow tunnel with reeking sulphur fumes which often took an hour or more to disperse. The committee, not called upon to breathe the air, was confident that 'small machines [which] will soon remove any difficulties of that sort'. It was far more worried by the problem of the water.

To provide sufficient power to operate water-wheels, completion of the cutting from the Abbey Bridge at Tavistock to the Lumburn Valley was expedited, and on 12 October 1805, in the presence of the entire committee of management, water was turned into it and the canal filled nearly to Crowndale. This brought an immediate and unexpected benefit. Goods being carried by packhorse from Morwellham could now be transferred to the canal at Crowndale to finish the remainder of the journey to Tavistock by boat. This 'back carriage', as it was called, proved surprisingly heavy and seemed an early justification for the cost and effort of building the canal.

By August 1806 reasonable progress was being made with tunnelling, and the entire undertaking had cost so far £15,091. But costs on several occasions had risen to 15 guineas for driving only a small level. This, together 'with the great hindrance caused by the water in Taylor's shaft' brought cries of despondency from the committee, which demanded the sinking of more shafts to 'secure a more rapid execution of the tunnel'. Serious thought was given to getting a big steam engine for pumping out water. At the same time the mining side of the enterprise was causing concern, and money from the canal account was diverted to shoring it up; the lodes at Wheal Crebor were playing hide-and-seek and £2,535 had been spent in development for a return of only £98.

The summer of 1807 was one of flaying heat. Workers fainted in the harvest field, the sun burned down all day, and the atmosphere in the airless smoke-filled tunnel was stifling. Nevertheless by August 435 fathoms had been driven in, and work on the open cutting between the northern end of the tunnel and Tavistock was complete apart from the aqueduct over the Lumburn. Altogether £21,000, over half the estimated amount, had been spent.

The year 1807 was indeed a trying year, but as 1808 approached, four years of incessant labour began to bear fruit, and the committee's spirits rose accordingly. By August of 1809 it could congratulate 'the proprietors on the near approach of the termination of the expenses of constructing the navigational work upon the surface'. The aqueduct had been completed and 'executed with the greatest attention to solidity of construction'. Great care had been taken to make it watertight, dozens of men being employed in puddling the clay to provide a strong lining. Baffles were provided at the Tavistock end to control the flow of water, and apart from a minor subsidence in the embankment soon after it was built the aqueduct has remained firm for the rest of its life.

VENTILATION AND DRAINAGE 'ENGINES'

Progress was also better in the tunnel. It was now 526 fathoms in and Taylor had overcome the twin problems of bad air and flooding. To ventilate the tunnel a 'special engine' he had constructed brought air down the shafts through a stream of water. The 'engine' was in fact a pump worked by a water-wheel, but instead of pumping fresh air into vitiated air Taylor's machine reversed the process, the upstroke of its cylinder sucking out the impure air at the rate of 200 gallons a minute, while fresh air brought in by the water was forced through a pipe on the downstroke. It was so successful that

within a very short time after the machine had begun working the whole extent of the tunnel which had been uninterruptedly clouded with smoke for some months before and which the air that was forced in would never drive out, now became speedily so clear that daylight and even objects at its mouth could be distinctly seen at its farthest end. After blowing up the rocks the miners could instantly return to the place where they had been employed unimpeded by the smoke of which no appearance would remain underground in a very few minutes while it might be seen to be discharged in gusts by the valve at the top of the shaft. The constant current into the pipe at the same time prevented the accummulation of air unfit for respiration. The influx of air from the level into the mouth of the pipe rushes with such force as instantly to extinguish the flames of a very large candle.

Three of these engines worked by water-wheels were set up on the course of the tunnel and the Royal Society of Arts awarded Taylor a silver medal.

To deal with the water, a wheel of 40 ft diameter and with a 6-ft breast was constructed at Gill & Bray's foundry at Tavistock and set up at the northern end of the tunnel. This, turned by the current from the canal, operated flat rods which, travelling 'over the ground on cast iron wheels contrived to revolve with as little friction as possible', operated Cornish pumps at the shafts. The wheel transmitted its power through $1\frac{1}{2}$ miles of these rods which ran uphill. The system proved extraordinarily cheap, efficient and trouble-free and excited admiration at the time as 'the greatest extension of motion that was ever attained'.

Solving these air and water problems proved a milestone in the canal's construction, and by 1810 it was navigable on the surface from the Abbey Weir at Tavistock to the tunnel's northern entrance. Boats were now needed, and the Mount Foundry Iron works at Tavistock was told to construct an iron one designed to carry

8 tons. About 38 ft long with a 15-ft beam, it was made of small pieces of sheet or boiler plate riveted together, and was launched on the canal on Easter Monday 1811.

In the tunnel itself, however, the scene was still hardly cheerful. It was becoming difficult to remove all the stone and rubble through the comparatively small shafts. Guttering candles fitfully lit a scene of almost Dantean gloom and oppressiveness. In a coffin-like space little more than 10 ft high and 7 ft wide, between thirty and forty men toiled and stumbled with picks, shovels and crude drills in a chaos of rubble, falling water and tumbling rock. The blasts from shot firing cracked and echoed around them, and Taylor's 'wind engine' so efficient in removing the smoke from these blasts blew out the men's candles unless the flame was closely guarded[5].

FINANCES

Along with the tunnel work had been going on to develop Wheal Crebor (see next chapter), and by 1810 nearly six years of patient effort began to reveal what were then the largest undivided copper deposits in the district. The increasing importance of Wheal Crebor lead to the creation of a separate mining account in 1812, and the appointment of a committee to manage the mines associated with the canal. In the next few years some of Wheal Crebor's considerable profits almost certainly helped towards the canal costs. It was not, however, an easy mine to work, and as late as 1812 the committee was gloomily noting that since its discovery Wheal Crebor had cost its adventurers £21,465 and 'there is still no expectation of any profit'.

Nor were the finances of the canal undertaking wholly satisfactory. In June 1813 when 900 fathoms of the tunnel had been excavated the total cost of the whole undertaking, including mining, was put at £47,000, or £7,000 above Taylor's estimate; dues from that part of the canal so far opened had brought in £638. A year later the canal's costs had advanced to £52,809 and it appears from the committee's minutes that there had been three calls on the shareholders, although the canal Act gave powers to raise a mortgage. In all the canal's shareholders appear to have paid £55 each over the £100 value of their shares.

But by June 1816 only 20 more fathoms of the tunnel remained to be driven and there were solid hopes of the work being completed by August.

> The only important work that now remains to complete the navigation to the Tamar will be the execution of a proper apparatus for passing the goods from the south end of the tunnel to Morwell quay. The very beneficial application of an incline plane at Wheal Crebor and at another mine in the neighbourhood has satisfied the committee of the propriety of adopting some similar plan.

The hope of finishing the tunnel by August was justified. On the 24th the *Annual Register* carried a brief announcement stating 'that stupendous undertaking the tunnel of the Tavistock Canal, was, after thirteen years of incessant labour, holed on the 21st with great accuracy. A line of communication has been established between the Tavy and the Tamar'. The management committee's own record of the achievement had a justifiable ring of self-appreciation.

> This operation terminates the labour of 13 years and the anxious care of those who had most nearly to contemplate the difficulties which attended it and to provide for their being surmounted. The Tavistock tunnel will be a lasting monument of the patience of those who executed it and of the spirit and enterprise of the proprietors who supported the work, and who have so steadily pursued their object through the disheartening circumstances which have of late attended all mining pursuits.

It was hoped the tunnel would be ready for boats by 17 February 1817. Nearly thirty years later, giving evidence before a government commission, Taylor said he could not recall a single fatal accident in the building of the canal.

THE INCLINE PLANE

It had come out into the daylight in a little hollow on the south side of Morwell Down nearly 240 ft above high water on the Tamar. All that remained now was to link it with the river and the committee confirmed the earlier decision to do this with an incline plane. A piece of open cutting was made from the south end to a point above Morwellham, where a water-wheel was erected in a specially constructed basin and a bypass constructed to bring the waste water of the canal to it. From here the fall to Morwellham was 237 ft 2 in, and a double-track incline was laid to connect the canal to the quays.

Two descriptions exist of this apparatus. One, by two Prussian engineers who saw either the incline or the plans for it in 1826 or 1827, describes a water-wheel 28 ft diameter which raised and lowered wagons over a double track of 3 ft 10 in gauge. The wagons, made of sheet iron and arranged for tipping, were drawn or let down by an iron chain supported on rollers.

> When a wagon came to the top of the tram road it automatically put the water wheel out of gear with the chain drum, the wheel continuing to turn. Hand gear was provided for the same purpose. The plane was 720 ft long and had a slope of 15 degrees.[6]

Hansford Worth, a Plymouth consulting engineer with antiquarian tastes, saw the incline in 1888 when it was ruinous, and described the gauge as 4 ft 3 in, the trucks running on it having one pair of wheels 4 in higher than the other to keep the body of the truck level on the incline. His description of the water-wheel and the winding machinery as he then saw it is worth quoting:

> The wheel itself . . . is about three feet breast and 25 to 30 feet in diameter. On its axle is fitted a somewhat ponderous bevelled cog wheel into which gears another of smaller dimensions. This is fitted on a stout wooden axle which rises almost vertically and moves by the aid of another

pair of bevelled wheels on another horizontal wooden axle. . . . On this last
is fitted a large drum on to which winds a chain of four inch link and three
quarter inch iron which used to draw the ascending trucks. . . . Another
large drum with a wire rope on it is so connected with this last by a pair
of ordinary toothed wheels that the descending train laden with copper ore
was made to assist the water wheel in drawing up the ascending trucks.

According to Worth the lines were rolled flat iron-head rails weighing about 25 lb per yard run, with chairs fixed by wrought iron
spikes to granite or slate sleepers[7].

It should be noted that the incline was repaired in the 1850s and
this may account for discrepancies between Worth's description and
the earlier one, but it seems clear that the canal barges were not, as
is widely believed, fitted with wheels to enable them to be transferred to the incline. Their cargoes were lifted from the barges to
the trucks, and to help in this a crane was put up on the canal wharf.
Taylor's estimate for building the incline was £2,900, of which
£1,800 was for constructing the plane, £100 for the winding chain
and £200 for the water-wheel.

THE CANAL AT WORK

The canal was officially opened on 24 June 1817, almost fourteen
years after it had been started. Nine tub boats carrying between 300
and 400 invited guests 'of all ranks' made their way along the waters
to the tunnel and as they entered that 'monument of industry and
perseverance with rather awful and sublime sensations', many put
up umbrellas to keep off the drips from the tunnel roof. To cheer
them a band of instrumentalists in several boats set up a rever-
berating din. Parties of miners and others had ribbons in their hats
bearing the words 'Success to the Tavistock Canal', and as the first
boat came out into the daylight cheers went up from nearly 5,000
people; 240 ft below at Morwellham quay, ships fired a twenty-one-
gun salute. Refreshments, toasts and dancing wound up the day and

launched an enterprise which was afterwards estimated to have cost 'upwards of £70,000'.

The canal began its working life at a time of depression. Land carriage had been cheapened by a fall in the price of fodder and the release of horses from Government work. As the committee soberly noted in the minute book:

> That the tonnage will fall very far short of the original estimate cannot be doubted; at a time when this was made the mines in the neighbourhood were in their most flourishing condition or rapidly advancing to it. Agriculture, encouraged by the high prices was improving everywhere, and the use of lime so essential to good cultivation of the soil of the district through which the canal passes, was very great and increasing. Slate quarries, then making very large returns, were in full activity, and new ones were opening. In all these sources of employment for an oeconomical [*sic*] mode of carriage, the greatest reverses have taken place and at present a stagnation of enterprise and consequent inactivity prevails.

So the authorized dues were cut to 1s a quarter for coal, limestone and slate; 1½d a bushel for lime and 1s 6d a ton for copper and lead. It was decided, courageously in the circumstances, to push on with the 2-mile cut to Mill Hill, completed by 30 January 1819. After this the canal paid a maiden dividend of £2 a share and went on to earn an average profit of £600 a year. The original estimate had been for £2,000.

The canal worked smoothly and comparatively expeditiously. On the return journey from Morwellham, boats were poled through the tunnel against the current and then hitched to horses for the remainder of the journey to Tavistock. The type of cargo carried is well illustrated by the tolls for 1819, the first year for which full figures are available. These included:

Sundries	6,747 tons
Granite	407 tons
Limestone	10,254 tons
Wheal Crebor ores	1,136 tons
Wheal Crowndale ores	242 tons

Wheal Friendship ores   2,502 tons
Pig lead   235 tons
Slates   48 tons

Most of the pig lead came from Wheal Betsy, but the small tonnage from the mines was a disappointment and the fact that the canal was only a modest financial success throughout its life was largely due to the unexpectedly short life of the Crebor and Crowndale mines. By 1828 the early workings at Crebor had closed entirely.

Another big disappointment was that the slump hit building enterprises, too, and caused the complete cessation of the carriage of granite, from which there had been high hopes. Thirty to 60 tons a day had been shipped down the Tamar from Dartmoor (probably from the Merrivale quarries) for the 'adornment of the metropolis', some of it going to build the Thames Embankment.

The trade depression persisted obstinately throughout the 1820s, agriculture being as badly hit as mining. The tonnage carried dropped each year, until in 1831 only 11,518 tons was sent over the canal and the dividend was cut to 30s. Those dues that were one-eighth were further reduced to one-quarter on condition that carriers reduced their charge to 2s 6d, but despite this the dividend three years later had dropped to £1. Bleak as the start was the 1830s, however, ushered in better times, and by 1835 the cargo carried had crept up to nearly 15,500 tons. In Tavistock itself more houses were springing up as the district became more settled and prosperous, and by 1837 a peak was reached with the carriage over the canal of 20,006 tons; limestone and copper from Wheal Friendship (6,000 and 3,936 tons respectively) and 9,136 tons of 'sundries' represented valuable money-earning cargoes. The scene at Morwellham was now a busy one, and the incline was constantly in use, three and four wagons being coupled together to form a train of both ascending and descending loads. The committee raised the dues from one-fourth to one-eighth again, and trade continued fairly steady, with an isolated peak of 20,149 tons in 1847. This was the third highest tonnage carried in any one year, and was due largely to the transport of granite from Dartmoor for public works at Devonport.

THE DECLINE OF TRAFFIC

It now became apparent, however, that the dues being charged did not reflect the increased trade. Between 1837 and 1841 they had returned between £1,000 and £1,100 a year, but in 1842, despite the carriage of nearly 16,000 tons, the return had dropped to £997. The committee had earlier agreed (1841) to let the canal to Messrs Gill & Rundle, the Tavistock carriers, for £700 a year, with extra payment if tonnage rose beyond a certain level. But it dropped instead, from a little over 10,000 tons in 1843 with dues at £711, to dues of only £626 in 1845. In a despairing gesture the dues for that year were cut to 1s a ton on all goods except for limestone which was accepted at 6d.

The failure of the mines for which the canal had largely been built was now complete. In 1825–59 only 371 tons of ore had been sent over the canal from Wheal Crowndale and 1,167 tons from Wheal Crebor. The only consistent producer had been Wheal Friendship, which over a similar period had sent some 70,000 tons of copper ore. Hopes were raised from a discovery of copper at Sortridge mine, Whitchurch, in 1859 but a shipment of 360 tons in September of that year proved an isolated peak. When under the stimulus of the working of Devon Great Consols, Wheal Crebor was revived in the 1850s as a 'very fair speculation', the railway was on its way to Tavistock as a competitor and the canal had little more than ten years of active life left. Railway competition had been casting a growing shadow since the early 1840s and became a fact in 1859, when the South Devon branch line from Plymouth to Tavistock was

Overgrown beehive type kilns of the old Calstock Fireclay works near St Anne's chapel (since demolished)

Partly demolished brick kilns and ovens on Hingston Down

Early nineteenth-century warehouses and cottages at the old Tavistock Canal wharf

Tavistock Canal aqueduct over the river Lumburn near Crowndale

opened. By 1865 it had been extended to Launceston and had begun to attract ominously heavy traffic.

To counter this, the machinery of the incline plane was repaired, and in 1854 water-wheels connected with a wire rope, to hasten the passage of boats, were put up at each end of the tunnel. The 4 miles of rope needed were made in Tavistock—the longest piece of rope ever made in the district it was asserted at the time—and the scheme cost the committee £200. But the ropes scored the sides of the tunnel causing frequent breakdowns and the system was abandoned[8]. In 1860, 14,410 tons of goods were carried, almost entirely made up of coal, limestone and copper ore from Wheal Friendship. To keep up with the remorseless railway, dues were cut again by 3d a ton, so that heavy goods were charged 4s a ton from Morwellham to Tavistock. This did raise the tonnage in that year to 18,140, but it was a peak never attained again; by 1868 a mere 9,812 tons was being carried. Wheal Crelake, near West Bridge, an active and productive mine in the 1860s and well placed for the canal, preferred the railway, sending its ores direct to Plymouth at special cheap rates.

Limestone and coal were almost all that now remained for the canal. Wheal Crebor, whose fortunes had revived again, began to send between 300 and 400 tons of copper ore a month to Morwellham, but this was offset by the almost total cessation of traffic from Wheal Friendship. An attempt to get the Duke of Bedford to reduce the dock dues at Morwellham proved fruitless, and the Mill Hill branch was now completely moribund through the failure of the slate quarries.

In 1870 the entries in the canal's books begin to get scarcer and scarcer, the clerk hardly bothering to keep the accounts. A mere 1,000 tons was carried in the year and it was proving difficult to get a quorum at management-committee meetings. By the end of the year the canal was offered back to the Duke, along with the remaining shares of £10 each. But he, seeing every likelihood of it reverting

H

to him without charge if things were left to go on a little longer, remained silent. After a further twelve months he offered £8 a share and half the cost of the Act transferring the canal to him. These terms were accepted, and on 17 May 1873 an Act was passed authorizing the sale of the canal to the Duke for £3,200, to be paid to the trustees of the company and distributed to shareholders after payment of debts. The Duke was not obliged to maintain the canal, which in the formal phrases recording its demise was by now 'wholly or almost wholly disused for the purposes of navigation'. A final dividend of £12 a share was distributed, and on 11 November 1873 the canal ceased to be an active navigation.

The Duke, for less than he would have paid for a good farm, had secured 4½ miles of navigable waterway and several cottages, while over £10,000 in royalties had been paid to his family from the mining ventures associated with it. By 1889 the waterway had disappeared from the list of canal returns.

NEW USES

Early in the present century Tavistock Urban Council bought the meadow lands adjoining the section running between Abbey Bridge and West Bridge and laid out ornamental gardens around it. In 1933, the West Devon Electric Power Company harnessed the canal's current to drive the turbines of its hydro-electric station on a disused copper quay at Morwellham. In removing over 20,000 tons of silt from the canal's bed for this purpose, a considerable quantity of coal was recovered, dropped from iron barges in the years of the canal's prosperity. At the Morwellham end the water was diverted from the old cut and two short new tunnels, 500 ft and 130 ft in length, carry it under the road and ridge of ground to a reservoir, from where the water is led by a 500-ft long pipe to two turbines at Morwellham. The station, the largest of its kind in

England, is now under the control of the Central Electricity Generating Board, which rents the canal for £1 a day.

Time has dealt gently with Taylor's masterpiece. Except for the diversion at Morwellham and the disappearance of the incline, it looks today much as it did in the 30s and 40s of the last century, when horses clip-clopped along its towpath, miners emerged in boats from its tunnel mouth and at Morwellham 'sailors whistled, workmen shouted and hammered and the laden trolleys rumbled up and down the incline'.

What its fortunes might have been had the mines connected with it thrived can be glimpsed by a comparison with the Looe Canal, which was also built to supply coal and agricultural lime to a farming interior and take away the produce of developing mines. In the five years 1849–54 (the Caradon copper mines which it served were discovered in 1837) the carriage over the Looe Canal grew from 24,000 to 36,000 tons a year, of which 16,000 tons were mineral ores. By 1856, when the Tavistock Canal was reducing its dues to keep alive, the Looe Canal was carrying 48,000 tons a year and the output of the Caradon mines was so taxing its capacity that a railway had to be built to take away the surplus.

It was this sort of trade John Taylor had in mind when he sat down in 1800 to prepare the preliminary sketches for a 'navigation from the Tavy to the Tamar'.

THE MILL HILL 'CUT'

This 2-mile branch from the Tavistock Canal was designed to serve the deep slate quarries at Mill Hill, where for over 400 years an outcrop of green and bluish-black slates with a good cleavage has been dug for building and other uses. In the eighteenth and nineteenth centuries Mill Hill slates were much fancied for cisterns and chimney pieces, and for hanging on west-facing walls. In the middle of the eighteenth century over 200 people were employed in the quarries, and until the Napoleonic wars there was a thriving export of slates to the Channel Islands.

At the beginning of the nineteenth century there were ambitious plans to increase the output of these quarries and the side 'cut' to connect them to the canal was begun in the autumn of 1817. The 'cut', which tapped the waters of the river Lumburn at Mill Hill, had the same dimensions as the Tavistock Canal, which it joined on the south side of the aqueduct; when work on it was completed by 1819 the total cost was noted as not exceeding £1,800. The original estimate had been for £1,435, of which £615 had been for an incline plane to surmount a rise of 19½ ft. A memorandum in the canal management minute book for 1817 states that the cut was paid for by 'income arising from the mines'.

The cut was never particularly successful, and provided more headaches than profit. The first year of its existence coincided with a drought and the owner of a corn mill along its course abstracted so much water that it nearly ran dry. The quarry owners were also uncooperative, seeming to prefer land carriage, although it was estimated that the canal rate worked out at 3s a ton compared with 'six shillings or seven shillings by any other mode'.

To encourage its use a lime kiln and a wharf were constructed at Mill Hill, but the estimate that the branch would contribute £600 annually to the revenue of the canal proved wildly optimistic. Continuing low prices in agriculture cut the demand for lime, and in 1821 tolls for its conveyance were cut from 1s to 6d a ton. The demand for slate from the quarries almost ceased and by 1830 the branch was virtually unused—large stretches being dry while in other places rank growth obstructed it. In 1844 a new company leased the quarries and, with the prospect of more building in the district and an increased demand for slate, the owners approached the canal company with a proposition to send all their goods over the canal to the Tamar at a flat rate of 2s a ton for ten years if the canal were reopened; alternatively, provision of a railway was requested. On the advice of John Taylor the waterway was abandoned and a horse tramway constructed on the embankment alongside for £1,200.

In midsummer 1846 the tramway was opened for traffic, all goods carried being charged 1s a ton. The canal company provided a crane at an unloading basin near the aqueduct. In 1847 803 tons of slate were carried, but three years later traffic had dropped to 623 tons; it dwindled steadily, until by 1860 the tramway was moribund. The rails were offered for sale (without success) to the Lee Moor Porcelain Company, owned by Lord Morley of Saltram, and when in 1873 the main canal was sold back to the Duke of Bedford the 'collateral cut to Mill Hill' was included in the price.

This little canal today provides an interesting puzzle: where along its route was the incline plane designed to surmount a rise of 19½ ft? Most of its length is easy to follow, although not identified on the current 6-in map. From the aqueduct to Lumburn Corner its route is plain, and it can be picked up again on the north side of the Tavistock–Gunnislake road by the outline of the embankment which formerly carried the horse tramway. This runs round the back of a now-disused corn mill, and crosses the road to skirt the edge of a wood until it reaches the crossroads at Middle Lumburn Bridge. Hereabouts, according to the original plan, was the incline plane, up and down which canal boats were hauled on special wagons drawn by horses. From this point the canal was planned to be carried on along an 'upper level to Mill Hill bridge', a distance of 633 yards.

Although the ground today affords few clues, the incline plane to lift the canal to the upper level seems to have been built near the disused quarry at this point. A report by the two Prussian railway engineers, Oeynhaussen and Decken, who saw the canal working, says the incline was a cast iron railway track 70½ ft wide and 156 fathoms long rising 1½ in in a fathom (1 in 48). 'A wagon about 20 ft runs along this track and can be lowered far enough into the water for the boat to rise by itself. Thus boat, load and wagon, about eight tons altogether, can be drawn from one part of the canal to the other by three horses. A horse pulls the empty boat up and the loaded boat down.' (I am indebted to Mr Charles Hadfield for this translation.)

The site is still difficult to identify, but this description provides firm evidence of the incline plane's existence. It was near the blocked bridge on the road to Chip Shop some 30 yd west of Middle Lumburn Bridge. The existing bed of the canal is on a course taking it under this bridge and from thence it probably led straight into the quarry workings along what is now the road in front of a row of cottages (put up between 1850 and 1860). Jutting out into this road, near the cottages, is a large wharehouse-like building known as the granary, and underneath it used to be a wharf or basin with mooring rings let into its walls. The basin was filled in 1912, but in a garden close by still stands the lime kiln built in 1819 to burn the stone unloaded by the canal boats at this wharf. In a few years all traces of this little waterway may well be completely lost.

THE TAMAR MANURE NAVIGATION

On the western bank of the Tamar a few hundred yards below Gunnislake Bridge is a half-dry cutting, 500 yd long, which by-passes the fish weir at Weir Head. At its southern end is a substantial lock and basin beside a group of ruined cottages, one of which belonged to the lock-keeper.

The cutting and lock basin are the only visible evidence of a grandiose scheme first discussed in 1794 to make a canal route from a point near North Tamerton Bridge (not far from the Tamar's source) to Morwellham, which was to be 30 miles 6 furlongs long, with a collateral cut of 1 mile 2 furlongs to Launceston. The company formed to carry out the scheme was empowered to raise £121,000 in £50 shares and to pay the Duchy of Cornwall £200 a year for the liberty of making the navigation.

The entire project almost immediately fell victim to the war with France. Then, in 1808, 'largely through the intervention of one of the proprietors', says Moore in his *History of Devonshire*, the 3-mile section between Morwellham Quay and Weir Head was completed at a cost of £11,000. This included digging 500 yd of cutting and building a lock 70 ft by 12 ft with meticulously squared blocks of granite. The company found, however, that the 'liberty of the navigation' meant holding in perpetuity from Lord Mount Edgecumbe and the Duke of Cornwall

> an expensive fishery on the river Tamar which is not, however, at present a source of the least profit, the reserved rents paid to the Lords in Fee being greater than the amount for which the company can now let the fisheries to the fishermen on the river.

In the 1850s the company claimed damages from the Devon Great Consols mine company for allowing mineral waste to pollute the river, turning the water milky-white and killing all the salmon. Because of mine pollution it was claimed the fishery had long been regarded as worthless[8].

The little Tamar Manure Navigation enjoyed a useful and exceptionally long life. Manure, building sand, bricks, lime and granite were carried until well into the present century, in barges which, for a wage of 1s 6d each, were hauled up from Morwellham against the current by teams of men pulling on ropes attached to the masts of the vessels. Gunnislake gas works, opened in 1872 with a display of fireworks, was supplied by coal from this canal up until the first world war. In 1905 traffic on the canal amounted to 7,740 tons, of which a third was coal and the rest bricks and granite. After the first world war the costs of dredging and clearing the channel and keeping the lock in repair were above the returns, and notices were exhibited at Morwellham and at the locks warning against its use. Soon after the second world war liquidation proceedings were started, and while these were being heard in London in 1942 an air raid is said to have destroyed the records and minutes of the company.

It is possible that this little canal worked with one of the earliest tramways in the Tamar Valley, for Moore mentions a railway built alongside it. He gives no other details but a clue may perhaps be found in Turner's picture 'Crossing the Brook', painted near this spot in 1815 and now in the National Gallery. This shows a landscape which has strong similarities to the Cornish bank of the Tamar below Gunnislake. Two water-wheels are depicted on a site which suggest they were part of the machinery of Gunnislake Old mine, which was working by water-wheels at this time. Below these wheels and running into the distance a tramway is plainly shown. Turner's painting is an idealized impression rather than a literal painting of what he saw, but if a tramway were then in existence on this site, this is the spot where one would expect to find it: for it would lead to a well-established quay at Netstakes below Weir Head, and it was near here in 1859 that the Slimeford manganese works at Gunnislake had a similar tramway.

CHAPTER SEVEN

The Canal Mines

ALTHOUGH the Tavistock Canal was as much a mining speculation as a transport venture, the immense labour of tunnelling under Morwell Down to exploit what was thought to be promising mineral ground was poorly rewarded. Only one of the six lodes found proved productive; it was developed as Wheal Crebor. On the other hand many of the mines indirectly associated with the project lived on long after the canal was abandoned despite their comparatively meagre contributions to its dividends. Wheal Crebor, which in its early years had iron boats built to carry its own ores over the canal, worked into the present century. Wheal Friendship, John Taylor's first love, was not finally abandoned until 1925. Nor were all the mines benefiting from the canal situated on its banks. Sortridge and Wheal Franco were some distance away between the Tavy and the foothills of Dartmoor, but used it as the cheapest way of getting their copper and tin to the Tamar. Others, like Bedford United, one of the largest copper and arsenic producers in the area, tapped its water power extensively through an ingenious system of leats.

WHEAL BETSY

Among the earliest mineral freights to be carried over the canal were lead and silver ores from Wheal Betsy (lead, zinc and silver) which holiday makers speeding along the road from Okehampton to Tavistock pass on their left below the slopes of Gibbet Hill. A ruined and decaying mine engine house built in the 1840s is almost all that survives on the surface. Through the ground here, coursing north by south, is an anciently worked lead lode from which Wheal Betsy, after being restarted in 1806, produced up to 400 tons of lead and 4,000 to 4,500 oz of silver a year. A snuff box made from silver taken from the mine about this time is in the Plymouth Museum. The Wheal Betsy lode is picked up again in adjoining Wheal Friendship, and for a time the two mines were worked under the same management.

Much of Wheal Betsy's coal and coke was carried over the Tavistock Canal and the expenses for this in February 1831 were £312. To offset this cost peat was cut on the moors and burned in the smelting works, an experiment which met with considerable success. The mine was restarted in May 1863 under the name of Prince Arthur Consols (with a new capstan rope manufactured for it in Tavistock—220 fathoms long and 14½ in round); it was run as a separate undertaking from Wheal Friendship. Between 1845–75 it raised 1,180 tons of silver ore yielding 540 tons of lead and just over 2,000 oz of silver. The lode has been followed and worked from fourteen levels for nearly three-quarters of a mile to a depth of 170 fathoms and its course can be traced on the surface today by a line of shafts. Five water-wheels were installed, ranging from 42 ft to 14 ft diameter, for pumping, milling and hauling, water being taken from the Tavy by a leat which originates at Tavy Cleave. Wheal Betsy closed about 1877.

WHEAL FRIENDSHIP

Wheal Friendship (copper, arsenic, lead and iron) at Mary Tavy worked for 130 years—longer than any other mine in the district. It was remarkable for its extensive use of water power, brought by two leats from the Tavy uniting to produce a 526-ft fall of water; this at various times worked seventeen overshot water-wheels. The largest, 51 ft by 12 ft, and one of three wheels pumping under-ground, replaced a steam engine.

John Taylor took over the working about 1798, and opened it up further in 1826 by sinking an additional haulage shaft about 420 yd south-east of the chapel adjoining the main road. This sloped 40 degrees. A contemporary description of it refers to it as being 7 ft high and 5 ft wide, traversed by a single tramway of 3-ft gauge. Four-wheel tipping wagons, holding from 20 to 25 cwt of ore, ran over it, the loaded ones drawn up by an iron chain operated by a 40-ft water-wheel controlled by a brake wheel. Some of the rails were laid on the bare rock bottom of the level.

The workings of Wheal Friendship extend both sides of the road through Mary Tavy but its main development was between the road and the Tavy Valley on the east. It exploited an interlaced pattern of lodes extending for nearly a mile westward from the Tavy Valley and was worked to 220 fathoms. The main lode varied from 48 ft to 8 ft in thickness. In 1865, two years after Taylor had died, it was estimated the mine had raised 145,805 tons of copper, 1,170 tons of lead, 120 tons of tin and 4,343 tons of arsenic worth £1,371,954 representing a profit of £289,808.

After a period of uncertain working Wheal Friendship was revived in the 1880s by the Devon Arsenic Company, which installed a new 40-ft water-wheel (said to be equal to a new 50-in Cornish pumping engine) to work shallow deposits. In this period was built Brenton's stack, at the end of a long flue from the arsenic plant, which was a dominating feature of the mine until demolished as a military exer-cise shortly after the last war. In the 1920s the mine was worked along with a neighbouring tin mine (Wheal Jewell); during this time 150 tons of arsenic a year were recovered and at least five years' reserves were estimated to be in the dumps. A slump in arsenic led to final abandonment on 31 July 1925. Complete production and profit figures are never likely to be known, but between 1800 and 1885 J. H. Collins estimated over 155,000 tons of copper was pro-

duced and 13,380 tons of arsenic. The total profit up to 1885 was
put at £307,712.

The most striking remains of this mine are the ruins of its arsenic
plant, steadily being pillaged for bricks. The massive 300-ft long
flue leading to Brenton's stack is still largely intact and with the
ruins of the condensing chambers forms some of the most considerable remains of arsenic burning in the neighbourhood. Most of
the mine machinery was sold for scrap metal in 1936–7. A settlement
about a mile away at Horndon, known as 'Miner's Town', was
originally built for Devon Friendship workers.

WHEAL CROWNDALE

About a mile south of Tavistock on the banks of the canal is
Crowndale mine (arsenic, copper, iron and tin), which worked lodes
traced almost continuously from Gunnislake. Opened in 1799,
probably on the site of older workings, its reputed profit of £300,000
in its first twenty years—the Duke of Bedford alone receiving
£16,000 in dues—was one of the reasons prompting the building of
the canal. Producing mainly copper and some arsenic, it was principally worked by water-wheels turned by the current of the canal,
which runs through the sett. Its smelting works put up in the 1830s
treated not only its own produce but that of other Tavistock mines.

By the time the canal was opened the richest years of Wheal
Crowndale were over. It was reorganized in 1850 by a company
which spent nearly £4,000 on it but received only £2,000 in sales.
A further attempt to work it was made in 1858 'by a spirited company of adventurers', the mine being regarded as 'very favourably
situated on the track of several lodes with a great deal of ground
unexplored'; but the Duke of Bedford was averse to its development
for fear 'that it might deface the scenery and beauty of Tavistock'—
an early example in the area of town and country planning. Crown-

dale never worked on any scale after this, but in 1924 some parts
were reopened from a shaft on the north bank of the canal and an
ore shoot opened up containing 15,000 tons of arsenic. Samples also
revealed a small percentage of gold and silver. Some open shafts
close to the main Southern railway line which runs through the
sett, some concrete foundations for machinery and the remains of a
dump by the canal are the only reminders today of a mine whose
lodes are estimated to have produced £1,000,000 sterling.

WHEAL CREBOR

Less than a mile from Crowndale the river Lumburn passes under
the canal on its way to the Tavy. On its west bank lies Wheal Crebor
(arsenic, copper, iron and tin) whose underground workings come
within 50 fathoms of those of Crowndale. The copper lode from
which it was developed was found a few fathoms in from the north
end of the Tavistock Canal tunnel, and was worked from four main
shafts and an incline shaft—which can be seen today, only 20 ft from
the northern entrance to the tunnel. This goes down to 54 fathoms
at an angle of 35 degrees.

Wheal Crebor was discovered in 1804 and in the following years
some token sales of copper were made. It took nearly eight years of
steady work and a large outlay to render it productive; no steam
power was used, and horse-hauling of ore from the shaft cost £14
per 500 kibbles. Work on the tunnel and on the mine under it
proceeded simultaneously. By 1810 sales of ore had returned only
£1,350: prices were low, owing to the fluctuating copper standard.
But between 1811 (by which time 1,300 tons of copper ore had been
taken) and 1817 Crebor became one of the leading Devon copper
mines; by June 1817 its sales had totalled over £98,000. Its development costs of £76,134 left a net profit to the adventurers of only
£21,900; but it appears from the accounts that some contribution

was made towards 'finishing the canal without additional burden to the holders of mining shares'.

The Crebor deposits, like other copper workings in the area, were shallow, the deepest shaft being 200 fathoms. By 1820 the deposits under the tunnel were nearly exhausted and eight years later the slump was making it almost impossible to sell the mine's surface machinery. For nearly thirty years it worked intermittently, on a very small scale, until in the 1850s under the stimulus of the success of Devon Great Consols mine it was vigorously worked in the eastern section adjoining the Lumburn river.

The original 40-ft wheel at the tunnel mouth was supplemented by another 16 ft by 4 ft to work the crushing mill. Haulage from the mine was principally effected by the water-operated incline plane which John Taylor, drawing on his Wheal Friendship experience, had installed in 1807. An unsuccessful westward extension of the workings, generally known as *West Crebor*, was undertaken in the 1880s, its solitary relic being the ruined engine house in a field near Gulworthy. But the ground near the Lumburn remained sufficiently productive for Wheal Crebor to occupy third place in 1886 in the copper ticketings at Truro. Then 3,104 tons were sold for £6,494, its ore at this time being richer in metal content than that of Devon Great Consols. In 1884–9 nearly 8,000 tons of copper were produced, the mine at this period being one of the few copper ventures in Devon and Cornwall paying dividends. Its career, however, was ending. By 1901 it had been 'ransacked in search of copper and mundic between the 60 and 132 fathom levels without success' and its returns for that year totalled only £618. As the Duke of Bedford's agent tartly remarked, 'No mine can expect to keep going on such returns,' and it was finally abandoned in 1902.

An eastward strike of the Crebor and Crowndale lodes was worked by *East Crebor*, identified today by a few mounds in a field in the Tavy Valley. This mine was flooded by the Tavy in July 1880 drowning three men, the water at the same time entering much of

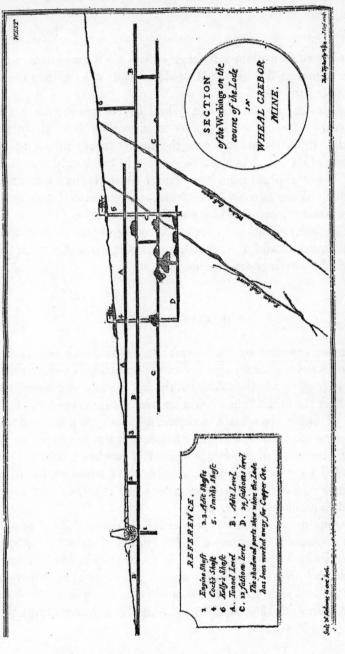

WEST

SECTION
of the Workings on the
course of the Lode
IN
WHEAL CREBOR
MINE.

John Taylor 1814 — 1 Inch scale

REFERENCE.

1 Engine Shaft   2.3. Adit Shafts
4 Cock's Shaft   5. Smith's Shaft
6 Kelly's Shaft
A. Tunnel Level   B. Adit Level
C. 12 fathom Level   D. 24 fathoms Level
The shadowed parts shew where the Lode
has been worked away for Copper Ore.

Scale 26 fathoms to one inch.

Section plan drawn for John Taylor in 1814 of Wheal Crebor Mine

the Crowndale workings. Its engine shaft, a few yards in off a farm track approached from the Walreddon road, still registers the rise and fall of the river.

Besides copper and arsenic, Wheal Crebor produced some tin, unusual in a mine situated over 2 miles away from the nearest granite. From the dumps near the tunnel mouth in the 1920s a 'sphere of tin ore almost too big to hold in two hands' was picked up[9]. The total profit from its workings has never been ascertained, although Moses Bawden, its last manager, estimated that altogether it produced 70,000 tons of copper which was sold for £500,000. The only surface remains of this mine today are its dumps close to the canal aqueduct and an interesting adit portal near the river from which the workings can be entered.

SORTRIDGE CONSOLS

On high ground by the Horrabridge–Whitchurch road 500 yd east of Sortridge Manor are the dumps of Sortridge Consols, a small copper producer in the middle of the last century whose ores were sent over the canal. When it was opened in 1854 copper was found only 5 ft below the surface in sufficient quantity to pay a dividend. 'No mine has started in brighter auspices' it was reported, but two years later much of its surface machinery was being sold off. This included a curious 'high pressure slide valve steam engine with a 11½ inch cylinder' built in Belgium and sent to this country for the Great Exhibition of 1851.

Despite the sale, small-scale working continued until 1859 when great excitement was aroused by the finding of copper in sufficient quantities at the 30-fathoms level for the mine to be looked upon as 'the second prize in the eastern district'; in September of that year over 300 tons were sent over the canal for smelting in South Wales. From then until 1869 nearly 8,000 tons of 7 per cent copper were produced. It closed in 1871 but was reopened in a small way in 1890 for tin and worked intermittently until 1902. Sortridge also produced small amounts of arsenic, for which its dumps were picked over in 1924. During the last war material from the dumps made some of the runways on Harrowbeer aerodrome at Yelverton.

EAST WHEAL RUSSELL

Above Morwellham at the south end of the canal tunnel is East Wheal Russell (copper and tin), part of whose workings connect directly with the tunnel. Josiah Hitchins, the discoverer of Devon Great Consols, had a particular interest in this mine; in February 1858 he held up a piece of gossan—an iron-stained stone—to a meeting of shareholders, declaring, 'If there is not a good lode of copper underneath this I was never more mistaken in my life.' A few months later four tributers, working at 66 fathoms, cut a rich lode of red, blue and grey oxide of copper estimated to be worth £200 a fathom, and in five weeks had cleared £1,000 between them as a result of their find. This was the height of the period of unscrupulous speculation in Cornish mines, and within a week East Wheal Russell shares had appreciated by £40,000 and the market value of a small and relatively insignificant mine stood at £90,000. At times the shares, manipulated by unscrupulous London brokers, fluctuated hourly.

During a little over ten years' working East Russell produced rather more than 9,000 tons of copper, sold for £49,863. Because of its position on high ground it was unable to use the waters of the canal either for pumping or for transporting the ores. All the work was done by three steam engines, at very heavy cost. This, with the cost of carriage of ores by road, swallowed up £54,000 by 1860—a sum only just covered by the receipts—with the result that no dividend could be paid. The mine was idle in 1871 and never satisfactorily reworked.

I

BEDFORD UNITED

Josiah Hitchins also had an active interest in Bedford United (arsenic, copper, fluorspar, iron, tin, uranium and wolfram), an important Devon mine situated on high ground immediately north-east of Gunnislake bridge, where five copper lodes traverse a 600-yd belt of country. Although nearly 2 miles from it, this mine used for much of its power the water from a leat cut from the Tavistock Canal above Morwellham. The leat follows the 200-ft contour of the hillside as if moulded into it, passing through two tunnels hollowed out of rock and in another case led across a rock face on wooden launders hung by chains. On the mine site the water drove two 46-ft by 2-ft water-wheels and supplied water for a 16-in winding and crushing engine. It was then diverted back across the main Gunnislake–Tavistock road to carry slime and waste to a dump by the river bank. Parts of this remarkable leat, which was in use up until the 1930s, can be traced on the present-day 2½-in map, but its course is best followed in its entirety on the 6-in map of 1907.

Bedford United was started in 1840 with work on the so-called Marquis lode, and the level leading into the hillside to explore it can still be seen with some of its original timbering by the river path above Gunnislake bridge. In twelve years from 1844 over 21,000 tons of copper were raised, from which dividends of £36,000 were paid, and the mine went on to become the third largest copper producer in Devon, having its own branch line to Devon Great Consols railway over which it secured an advantageous rate of carriage. It worked intermittently down to 1925, when 120 tons of arsenic was being produced a year and a special plant on the mine treated wolfram, tin and iron ore. The remains of this plant, together with a Cornish beam engine used for draining the mine, were still on the site in 1938 but were afterwards sold for scrap.

OTHER MINES

An old mining sett purchased by the original canal company was *Ding Dong* immediately south of Bedford United. It is linked by an adit with *East Luscombe* mine which, early in the nineteenth century, was associated with *North Impham*, a copper working about one-quarter of a mile south-east of Gunnislake on the Devon bank of the river—its gaping adit entrance can be seen close to the river bank. North Impham, once considered 'rich', yielded mainly copper; it has probably not worked for well over a century. East Luscombe, from one of whose shafts near Gulworthy Cottages wisps of vapour rise on a cold day as the warm air in the workings mingles with the surface atmosphere, was abandoned in 1827 because a channel of elvans 'cut into the richest ore of the lode and destroyed the ore'. On the same lode as Wheal Crebor, it was worked by the Williams family who then owned the prosperous Old Gunnislake mine.

Ding Dong, little more than an adit trial for copper, was reopened in 1915 and then again in 1942 by widening the adit, when about 1,000 tons of wolfram was obtained. The adit comes out into the river meadows just below Gunnislake bridge and runs under the hill towards Gulworthy, where in an adjoining plantation called Hatchwood the remains of the hoisting gear used over the shaft in the last war still exist.

Between Morwellham and Newquay on ground overlooking the Tamar are the scattered dumps of the old *George & Charlotte* mine (named after the sixth Duke of Bedford and his wife), whose sett—along with that of *Holming Beam*—the canal company bought in 1806 for £3,779. Originally opened up by adits driven on the eastern slopes of the Tamar Valley, it was drained in 1868 by three large water-wheels and a steam engine, and had returned a net loss of £27,135 'more attributable to mismanagement on the part of the

THE
DEVON GREAT UNITED COMPANY,
LIMITED.

Incorporated under the Companies' Acts, 1862 and 1867, whereby the Liability of Shareholders is limited to the amount of their Shares.

CAPITAL, £24,000, IN 12,000 SHARES OF £2 EACH.

10s. to be paid on Application and 10s. on Allotment.   No further amount of Capital is likely to be required or called up beyond this £1 per Share in the year 1880.

DIRECTORS.

THE RIGHT HON. LORD CLAUD HAMILTON,
HUGH STANLEY MORRIS, Esq.,
HENRY RICHARD TREHERN, Esq.,
SAMUEL YORK, Esq., Merchant, Wolverhampton.

} Directors of the
Devon Great Consols Company,
Limited.

BANKERS.
ALLIANCE BANK, LIMITED, LONDON, E.C..

SECRETARY.
Mr. W. H. ALLEN (Secretary to Devon Great Consols Co., Limited).

SOLICITOR.
G. H. BARBER, Esq., 34, Old Jewry, E.C.

OFFICES.
18, AUSTIN FRIARS, LONDON, E.C.

THIS Company has been formed for the purpose of purchasing the plant, machinery, licences, and leases of setts or mines, heretofore called the West Maria, Wheal Fortescue, and Wheal Williams (with the additional ground thereto), under leases to be granted by the several lords for twenty-one years, viz.:—Messrs. Willesford, Right Hon. Earl Fortescue, and the Duchy of Cornwall, and for working or developing the said mines, or any part thereof, as may be deemed desirable. The whole properties, including the machinery, are offered for the sum of £6,000 to a Company, to be called the Devon Great United Company, Limited; and that the Devon Great Consols shareholders shall have the first option of subscribing for 10,240 shares, being a *pro rata* interest of the share in the Devon Great Consols Company.

During the last workings, a part of the property was known as West Maria and Fortescue Consols; and from those workings, nearly all above the moderate depth of a 71-fathom level, copper ore and arsenic were sold amounting to about £45,000.

These mines are situated immediately to the west, and adjoining the celebrated Devon Great Consols (which, on an outlay of £1 per share of £10,240, has given in dividends £117 3s. per share, or £1,199,616). The copper ore and arsenic above referred to were produced not more than about 150 fathoms immediately to the west of where the Devon Great Consols made its first grand discovery.

One of the main objects in starting the late West Maria and Fortescue Consols was to drive west to the cross-course which passes through this and Wheal Williams; but owing to a disagreement with one of the lords, all operations westward were suspended. They were, however, resumed during the late great depression in mining, and up to June, 1877, about 50 fathoms had been opened on the north lode, and from one stope in bottom and back of the 71-fathom level, copper ore and arsenic were sold amounting to about £9,000. In the last report, presented by the agents on 27th June, 1877, we find the following:—"The 81 and 60-fathom levels west should be more particularly driven. In such case good discoveries will be made for copper ore, as the lode in the stope in the back never looked much better than at present, and is going up in whole ground, and no level driven over it. This is also the case with the run of ore gone down in the bottom of the level, and no end has ever been driven in under it. So we believe, if the 81 were driven west, a good lode must be reached; and it is a pity but this and other work could be done, seeing that the 71 has only been laid open for about 50 fathoms, and of this 30 fathoms long is productive ore ground, and no work to speak of has been done on this lode either above or below this level (71)."

It is well known that immediately to the west of the first great discovery in Devon Great Consols, the large lode divided, and in going westward formed several large and well defined lodes, the whole of which must of necessity go through the entire length of the amalgamated setts now to be worked, and known as the Devon Great United Mines. The main parts go back through the Wheal Williams portion of the mines, and were spoken of by the late Capt. James Richards, Manager of Devon Great Consols, in a report he wrote on the property June, 1872, extracts of which are as follows:—"Wheal Williams.—This mine is situated at Latchley, in the parish of Calstock, immediately to the west of Devon Great Consols. The sett is also very extensive, and is traversed by lodes of the most promising character, which, on being fairly developed, will, there can be no doubt, prove of great value. There are three lodes laid open. The north one having yielded several parcels of ore almost close to the surface, and the middle, or Orchard lode, is one of the finest I have ever had an opportunity of inspecting. This lode is 6 feet wide, composed of fine light capel, a quantity of mundic, quartz, prian, and good stones of both copper and tin ores, precisely similar in character to the lode found at the same depth at Wheal Anna Maria, a portion of Devon Great Consols Mines, and which has yielded and still continues to yield immense quantities of ore." In this report he further states: "The whole of these lodes are intersected by cross-courses, and looking at the indications presented at all points, *I can with confidence recommend this as one of the most promising investments in mining*."

The late Capt. James Phillips, of Bedford United Mines, writing on Wheal Williams, on the 24th February, 1865, says: "This concern deserves a spirited outlay, and the result will, no doubt, be a profitable mine."

Capt. Thomas Richards, of Hingston Down Consols, writing about Wheal Williams in 1865, says:—"It adjoins Devon Great Consols to the west, and is a very extensive sett, containing several lodes of the highest promise, the whole of which pass directly through the Devon Great Consols; and being in the same channel of ground as those mines, with two well-defined intersecting cross-courses, it will undoubtedly become, on being fully developed, a property of very great value."

Capt. William Clemo (an agent of Devon Great Consols) in a report states, in 1865, under the head of Wheal Williams, an extract of which is as follows:—This mine is situate almost close to the Devon Great Consols westward; and judging from the size and character of the lodes laid open, and the killas—which is of the most congenial kind for the production of mineral—I think that this sett is as much worthy of a trial, and is likely to turn out well, as any that can be found in the whole neighbourhood."

It is a notable fact that nothing has been done in Wheal Williams (except selling nearly the whole of the old burrows for arsenical mundic) since the foregoing reports were written. The late West Maria and Fortescue Company aequired the Wheal Williams sett, with the intention of cross-cutting south to intersect *the main part of the Devon Great Consols rich lode*, but this was never carried out.

There is a large quantity of machinery on the mines, comprising a 56-in. cylinder steam pumping engine with two boilers; a 14-inch rotary engine; a 24-inch winding engine; Cornish crusher; Brunton's calciner for manufacturing arsenic soot; twelve head stamps, complete; 90 fathoms 14 inches plunger lifts, complete; 45 fathoms of 10-inch and 8-inch drawing lifts, steam capstan, &c.; forming a large part of the plant for a productive and extensive run of mines, which these amalgamated setts will undoubtedly become.

The only contract entered into is an Agreement dated the 13th day of May, 1880, and made between William Mathews, Moses Bawden, and Peter Watson, of the first part; and John Horne Rowntree, on behalf of the Company, of the second part.

In the event of no allotment being made, the deposit will be returned in full. Application, with a deposit of 10s. per share, should be made in the accompanying form, and sent to the bankers of the Company.

Prospectuses and Forms of Application can be had from the Secretary, at the Offices of the Company, 18, Austin Friars, E.C., where prints of the Memorandum and Articles of Association, and a copy of the said Agreement of the Thirteenth day of May, 1880, can be seen.

The following report from Capt. Isaac Richards, the resident manager of Devon Great Consols, speaks for itself as to his opinion of the value of the Devon Great United Mines.

Devon Great Consols, May 7th, 1880.

DEVON GREAT UNITED COMPANY, LIMITED.
This property, which is situated immediately to the west of the northernmost portion of the celebrated Devon Great Consols, is of considerable extent, embracing the two setts formerly known as West Maria and Fortescue (from whence, although the workings were prosecuted on a comparatively limited scale, large returns of copper ores and arsenic have been made), and Wheal Williams immediately adjoining on the Cornish side of the River Tamar.

Comprised in this sett are several known well-defined and promising lodes, the mineralogical characteristics of *which are precisely similar to those of Devon Great Consols*, and the situation is such as not to admit of a doubt that the main lode of these great mines passes into and through this property.

There are also two cross-courses intersecting the lodes, and the strata being in all respects similar to that in which the lodes have been found productive in the leading and most productive mines of the district, this property presents such a field for mining enterprise as cannot in my opinion fail, if properly developed, to be attended with important and profitable results.   ISAAC RICHARDS.

The report of Capt. William Clemo (an agent who has been at Devon Great Consols Mines almost from the commencement) also speaks for itself, as to his opinion of the Devon Great United Mines:—

Devon Great Consols, May 6th, 1880.
I beg to hand you my report of West Maria Mine, which I have had frequent opportunities of inspecting as toller for Messrs. Willesford, the proprietors of the land.

The mine is situated immediately adjoining Wheal Maria, where the first splendid discovery was made in Devon Great Consols. There are several lodes passing through the sett. These lodes are in a channel of ground precisely similar to the ore-bearing killas of Devon Great Consols, and to the west of the present workings is a very fine cross-course from which lead has been raised and sold. All of the lodes have produced large quantities of copper ore as well as arsenical mundic of very superior quality. There is a long tract of ground westward which has never been tried, and looking at the congenial nature of the country, the size and character of the lodes, and the fine cross-course passing in that direction, I am firmly of opinion that a trial of this ground will lead to further important discoveries.

The machinery on the mine is good and strong. The dressing-floors and other requirements are well laid out, and are sufficient for an extensive working of this most promising property, the present proprietors having acquired the lease of Wheal Williams and ground to the west, and on which I have previously reported. I have no hesitation in saying that I consider the amalgamated setts through which *the main lode of Devon Great Consols must of necessity pass*, to be such a mining property as is not often presented to the public.

WILLIAM CLEMO.

London: Printed and Published by the Proprietor, WILLIAM DUNBAR QUINLAN, at the Offices, 241 & 242, Gresham House, Old Broad St., E.C., Saturday, May 22, 1880.

Prospectus issued in 1880 for Devon Great United Mine, a short-lived copper and arsenic working to the west of Devon Great Consols

officers than the poverty of the ground'. In fact receipts from copper ores had totalled over £61,000 in seventeen years' working from 1851 when nearly 16,600 tons of copper ore were raised. From this mine miners from Morwellham would often take a short cut underground into the workings of the adjoining William & Mary mine in the Tavy Valley.

Just south of George & Charlotte, the important *Gawton* mine (arsenic, copper, iron and tin) was, with Devon Great Consols, the leading arsenic producer in the district. Men working by the river in its King's shaft could hear the thump of paddle wheels above their heads as steamers passed. Gawton was an old copper working restarted in 1846 as a result of the discovery of Devon Great Consols, whose company spent over £800 enlarging Gawton Quay to take their surplus copper ore. By 1870, when it was 90 fathoms deep and employing 100 people, it had incurred a loss of nearly £21,000. In 1883 it became a limited company and was worked as such until 1893.

Despite its yield of over 20,000 tons of copper, worth nearly £31,000, between 1876–90, it was never a completely successful mine. It produced over 17,000 tons of arsenic worth nearly £180,000 between 1881 and 1902, and the buildings put up for refining arsenic are among the chief remains today. Particularly conspicuous is the flue which winds up the hillside above the Tamar to end in a prominent stack whose slant is said to be due to the cement on the south side drying out before that on the north when it was put up in the 1890s. King's shaft, immediately on the river bank, had to be protected from the wash of steamers and high tides by fascines. Gawton's dumps are a feature of the landscape on the east bank of the river above Calstock and are estimated to contain 124,000 tons of material. In the 1920s they were treated in a small way for copper precipitate.

Although not connected with the canal, the *Devon Great United* mine immediately west of Devon Great Consols is interesting be-

cause of the remains of its arsenic flue, almost lost among dense
growth, and its precariously leaning chimney. Because it adjoined
Devon Great Consols and because its geological characteristics were
similar great hopes were entertained of it in the 1880s, but its
working was bedevilled by disputes with landowners and it was
never a major producer. It had its own Brunton calciner for manufacturing arsenic soot. The remote and sheltered countryside around
is typical of the sylvan surroundings among which arsenic was produced in the Tamar Valley.

CHAPTER EIGHT

Devon Great Consols Mine

EARLY in 1900 the pumps of Devon Great Consols mine, near
Tavistock, stopped working for good. Today, sixty years afterwards,
copper precipitate still runs to waste unheeded from it, while its
dumps are estimated to contain nearly £4,000,000-worth of re-
coverable minerals. Prodigal of wealth even in its tumbled, tawny
ruin and decay, Devon Great Consols mine made the Tamar Valley
into a legend. For almost twenty years it was the richest copper mine
in Europe, and when its lodes began to fail it went on to produce
so much arsenic that the supply had to be regulated to avoid swamp-
ing the market.

'A mine of mines' was the way Peter Watson, its enthusiastic
managing director, described it in 1880; yet in many ways it was
unlike any other mine in the neighbourhood. Although physically in
Devon, its lodes originated in the granite across the river at Gunnislake, and because its ores were sold either in Truro or Redruth it
was invariably classed as a Cornish mine.

It was the only mine in Devon and Cornwall to build and work
its own standard-gauge railway. In its own foundry it maintained
and partly constructed many of the steam engines and water-wheels
used for pumping and for crushing ore. Tavistock was adorned and
improved from its royalties; in the days of its prosperity it circulated
£10,000 a month in the district. Its final closure in 1903 left a social
and economic void around Tavistock which has never yet been
satisfactorily filled.

Devon Great Consols also dispelled for ever the belief that no
rich mine would be discovered east of Truro. This was a view
widely held in the beginning of the nineteenth century. Until the

1830s, the dominance of the far western area of Cornwall in copper
production was absolute. In the decade 1801–10, Cornwall had
produced more than two-thirds of the world's entire copper output
of 91,000 tons, the contribution of the Devonshire mines, almost
all of which were in the Tamar Valley, being a mere 4,500 tons. But
as the Cornish mines went deeper, they also became more expensive
to work and the metallic quality of the ore became poorer. With
less profit being returned from the ore raised, prospectors turned
more and more to the eastern half of the county, particularly to the
country around St Austell and Liskeard, where the granite outcrops
were strikingly similar to those of the Carn Marth and Land's End
districts, the situation of most of the older mines.

Promising deposits of high-grade copper ore had been discovered
at Gunnislake before the end of the eighteenth century, but the
eastward shift began to be noticeable in 1811 when the first sales of
copper ore were made from Crinnis, near St Austell. This mine,
which in 1808 had been contemptuously described as 'not worth a
pipe of tobacco'[1], had become by 1828 fourth in the list of productive mines in Cornwall and had paid dividends of £240,000.
Close behind came Fowey Consols, prodded into life and great
wealth by the energetic and domineering J. A. Treffry. Then in
1837, the discovery of the Caradon mines on the bleak and treeless
Caradon moor started the great complex of workings that were to
become the Caradon mines. Devon Great Consols was the last great
copper discovery in the West of England and for twenty years from
1845 till 1865 the seemingly inexhaustible deposits overlaid the
copper-mining world.

RICH BEGINNINGS

Blanchdown Plantation, where the mine was discovered, is a leafy
coppice still preserving its name on the map. Miners had long

recognized the heaps of cindery gossan then littering the ground here as the surface 'cap' of copper deposits underneath. In the middle of the eighteenth century a solitary shaft had been sunk into this gossan, but it was abandoned at 14 fathoms although the debris from it was rich in copper indications. Pleas in the early nineteenth century by the Williams family, who owned the Gunnislake Old mine opposite Blanchdown, to rework the shaft were rejected by the sixth Duke of Bedford who had developed Blanchdown as a game preserve with over 40 miles of drives. He wanted 'no gang of miners disturbing his pheasants'[2].

But his successor, Francis Sackville, the seventh Duke, an aloof fastidious man, was more open to bargaining—on his own terms. In March 1844 Josiah Hugo Hitchins, a well-known Tavistock mining personality, secured from him an authorization to work the Blanch-down sett for twenty-one years on payment of dues of one-twelfth on all ores received. Hitchins, with five others, most of whom were London stockbrokers, formed a joint-stock company with 1,024 shares of £1 each, of which he himself held 144[3].

The new venture was first known as North Bedford Mines or Wheal Maria. Operations began on 10 August 1844 under the super-vision of 'Captain' James Phillips, manager for many years of the adjoining Bedford United Mines in which Hitchins was a share-holder. Captain Phillips noted in his diary the loan on that day of 162 lb of miners' tools, six pick hilts, three shovel hilts and three shovels. Work on the sett—3 miles long and 2 miles wide—started by digging pits to trace the lode and by enlarging the old shaft to working dimensions of 10 ft × 6 ft. On 19 August candles were being issued and a week later powder and safety fuse; by 4 November the shaft had been deepened another $2\frac{1}{2}$ fathoms. As the after-noon shift of the day laboured on with pick and shovel in the growing dusk, there was a sudden inrush of water. The back of what was to prove the longest and richest unbroken sulphide lode in South Western England had been struck, and by the time the shift had ended at 10 o'clock that night £60 worth of ore had been brought to the surface for an expenditure of little more than £200. The new working was given the name of Wheal Maria, after Hitchins's wife, and the shaft became Gard's shaft, after Richard Gard, then MP for Exeter, a London discount broker, who held 288 shares.

The richness of the find—the lode was to prove over 40 ft thick in places—astonished even Hitchins and the news of its discovery created a sensation. Memories went back to records of 100 years earlier when Wheal Virgin in West Cornwall was similarly discovered and in the first five weeks of working had produced £15,000 worth of ore at a cost of about £200[4]. At Blanchdown the ore was so abundant that its handling was a problem. Apart from the picks and shovels of the miners engaged, the only equipment at this stage was a small blacksmith's shop, roughly built of any gossan that lay to hand, where tools were sharpened. The ore standing solid in the shaft had to be dumped in heaps among the trees.

> So sudden and unexpected had been the discovery and in such quantities was the ore being thrown up that the place was crammed with copper, the richest yellow sulphuret in appearance and much more resembling heaps of gold than the baser metal and representing a combination of gorgeous metallic wealth and sylvan beauty the like of which will never be seen again.[5]

To overcome the water, which at first completely filled the shaft, a small water-wheel was put up and this 'with an apparatus of pumps, a whim and a capstan' constituted the only plant at Wheal Maria in its early days. By 20 February the first sales of nearly 192 tons of ore had realized £2,095. The ore yielded 17 per cent of copper and at £10 18s 6d a ton it commanded a price well above the average.

The lode, which was eventually to be proved on the Devon side for over 2 miles, with copper-ore pitches yielding between 10 to 15 tons to the cubic fathom, was driven on eastwards for 16 fathoms when it was suddenly lost, through being shifted 75 fathoms to the south by the Great Cross Course, a geological fault 18 ft wide.

With previous mining misfortunes in mind something like panic prevailed for several days until the lode was discovered again east of the fault. Here a second working was established, to the south-east of Wheal Maria, and given the title of Wheal Fanny, after Hitchins's infant daughter. In quick succession, as the lode was followed eastward, other mines to exploit it came into being: Wheal Anna Maria, named after the seventh Duchess of Bedford, Wheal Josiah after Hitchins himself, and finally at the eastern end of the sett, Wheal Emma, opened in 1848 and named after Mrs William Morris, mother of the poet, and whose husband was a shareholder. The whole group of mines was in 1846 named the Devonshire Great Consolidated Copper Mining Company. In that year the company sold 13,292 tons of ore, realizing £116,068, and paid a record bonus in dividends of £72,704 without having made any call on the original £1 shares. Shares which twelve months earlier Hitchins had vainly hawked around Tavistock were changing hands at £800 each.

From the start the mines were skilfully directed; nor was shortness of capital, which bedevilled so many other mining enterprises in the neighbourhood, a serious difficulty, the size and richness of the deposits giving the company ample liquid funds for development. Moreover expenses from the start had been astonishingly low. The ore in Gard's shaft had been less than 20 fathoms from the surface and above the natural level of drainage, so that Wheal Maria's early pumping costs were small. By March 1845 only £2,605 had been incurred in expenses, which partly accounted for the record dividend of nearly £73,000 paid in the first full working year.

But as the exploration went eastward so the mines deepened, the productive portion of the lodes extending to a greater depth in each mine. At Wheal Maria ore had been found at between 10 and 50 fathoms; at Wheal Fanny it was found within 16 ft of the surface, extending in a steeply pitching lode to 55 fathoms; and at Wheal

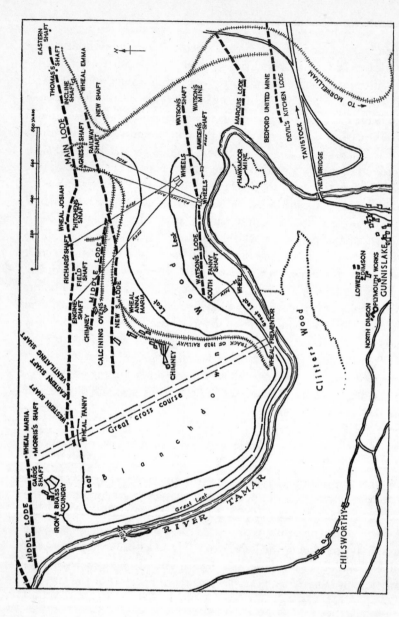

Plan of Devon Great Consols Mine based on 1880 ordnance survey and a Bedford estate map c. 1850–60

Emma, over a mile away from Wheal Maria, it was found at 60 to 132 fathoms. Had operations started here, Wheal Maria might well have remained undiscovered.

RISING COSTS

These deeper workings called for extensive pumping and surface works. The 'oak coppice, formerly tenanted by the hare and the woodcock and rarely visited save by the woodman or some solitary sportsman, rapidly became crowded with all the paraphanalia of a great and growing mine'. Among the 'paraphanalia' were steam engines for pumping installed in 1847 at Wheal Maria and Wheal Josiah at a cost of £2,180. Two more were erected at Wheal Anna Maria and Wheal Emma for £1,111 19s 10d.

Coal for the engines worked out at between 4s 6d and 5s a ton; ketches and schooners from South Wales sailed up the Tamar to unload it at Morwellham. The sums paid out for pumping, surface works, landing dues, carriage and other expenses began to be reflected in the mine's costs, which in the year ending March 1846 had been £30,590 but by 1848 had jumped to £57,000; dividends fell, and this coupled with malicious jealousy over the success of the mine, caused shares to slump from £800 to £135. There were hints that it was too rich to last. A gentleman writing over the alarming pseudonym of 'Typhoon' circulated a letter alleging that the mine was on the point of collapse.

To help offset the inevitably higher costs, it was decided in 1849 to harness the passing Tamar to help in pumping and hauling. This was done largely on the advice of Nathaniel Smith, the chief engineer of the Devon Friendship mine which employed some of the biggest water-wheels in the country. Accordingly on 20 March 1849 permission was obtained from the Duchy of Cornwall to draw water from the river for sixteen years for £250 a year, and the mine obtained all its basic power in the most prosperous years of its existence for only £5 a week. The lease was renewed at intervals, the rental being increased to £450 and then to £460 a year.

To bring water to points where it could operate machinery sometimes 400 ft to 500 ft above the river level three leats were cut, the biggest or Great Leat, 2 miles long and 18 ft wide, being fed from a weir at Latchley on the Tamar about a mile upstream from Wheal Maria. Another, the Upper Leat, was supplied from a storage reservoir, while a third or Lower Leat took waste water from Wheal Anna Maria dressing floors. These last two leats were, between them, $6\frac{1}{2}$ miles long.

The Great Leat, misleadingly marked on present-day maps as an 'old canal', was completed in 1849 and supplied a water-wheel 40 ft × 12 ft erected in a pit a little to the east of Blanchdown Farm; this pumped water from three shafts at Wheal Josiah and Wheal Maria. A second similar wheel was later put up 50 ft away as one of Wheal Josiah's shafts grew deeper.

Both these wheels turned at four revolutions a minute on 5-ft thick reinforced oak axles. A crank at either end of the axles had a stroke of 42 in or 48 in as required. Developing 140 horse power, each wheel could lift 52,000 lb of water at each stroke. Power was transmitted from the wheels to the pump shafts, nearly half a mile away, by a line of wrought iron flat rods $3\frac{1}{4}$ in thick, working over pulleys fixed on wooden supports which carried them 2,376 ft uphill to Wheal Maria and 2,160 ft to Wheal Josiah. At Wheal Maria 400 gallons of water a minute was lifted by this means from 480 ft, and from Wheal Josiah 270 gallons from 690 ft, the water being laid on to the wheels at 20 degrees from the summit. The weight of the pump rods was partially balanced by bobs placed near the wheel and this held the transmission rods in tension.

These two wheels had an overall efficiency of about 60 per cent and with their ponderous, majestic and measured motion, turning unceasingly night and day, they were one of the sights of the mine, shown to all visitors. A model of one of them existed in the Science Museum at South Kensington until destroyed in an air raid in the second world war.

The mine's foundry machinery was worked by a 35 ft × 45 ft wheel. A wheel 30 ft × 10 ft and developing 80 horse power, pumped water from Agnes shaft (184 fathoms deep), while another, 30 ft × 16 ft, forced 500 gallons of water a minute through a column of cast iron pipes from the Tamar, to a supply reservoir 1,200 ft away at Wheal Josiah. From here the water worked saw mills, a large hammer, lathes, and punching and cutting machines, before being guided by leats to the foundry and fitting shops at Wheal Maria, from where it was returned to the Tamar. Altogether the river water powered thirty-three wheels on the mine. In 1856 the efficiency of the big pumping wheels was further improved by a Tavistock carpenter, John Vigurs, who by 'linking the motion of the pump rod to the axle of the wheel' enabled water power hitherto solely used for pumping to be utilized for hauling from the shaft at the rate of 15 kibbles an hour. This was estimated to save £300 a year and Vigurs received the congratulations of the company at a dinner at Tavistock provided in his honour.

By 1850—little more than five years since the mine had been discovered—nearly 90,000 tons of copper ore had been sold, for which, after paying all expenses, the company had received £300,000. The Duke of Bedford had been paid £44,000 in royalties, while the shareholders had received about £207,000.

The main lode had been proved eastwards for nearly 2 miles. Between 20 and 40 fathoms down it passed in places into compact masses of copper and iron pyrites enclosed in a wall of arsenical pyrites between 5 ft and 6 ft thick which for the first twenty years of the mine's life was left standing. The men, working in levels 7 ft high and 4 ft wide, often found the ore compacted into solid bunches which left huge cavities when excavated. The softness of the ground often caused the walls of the levels to collapse, so 'underhand'

stoping had to be resorted to, the ore being dug out downwards
from the floor of the level instead of from the roof of the working
face. One of these cavities at the 150-fathom level was 900 ft long,
240 ft high and varied in width from 6 ft to 50 ft. Over two-thirds
of its contents were sent to market. Timber in baulks, often over
50 ft long and 2 ft square, was used to support the walls of these
excavations giving something of 'the appearance of the aisle of a
cathedral church'. Special cargoes of red pine from the Baltic were
obtained, although the particularly large timber needed to support
the dangerously soft ground in some of the excavations had to be
shipped from the Pacific coast of Canada. In 1859 the cost of this
American timber alone was £3,500.

THE BEDFORD HARVEST

In the year ending 1 March 1857 the company produced the
record total of 28,836 tons of copper ore, worth £158,432. In its
first twelve years it had sold ore worth over £1,400,000, or £35,000
more than Dolcoath's total output in the forty years after Waterloo.
Each of the five mines was now fully productive and the reserves in
Wheal Josiah alone were valued at £134,000.

The excitement of the original discovery had led to a rush for
mine setts on any piece of land adjoining Devon Great Consols.
Near-derelict mines like Wheal Crebor, Crowndale and George &
Charlotte, all on or near its perimeter, began to be looked at with
fresh interest. With the knowledge that land nominally valued at
14s 11d an acre might yield minerals improving its value to £1,235,
large sums of money were offered to the Duke for exploiting the
unproved land east of Wheal Emma. This, however, the Duke had
promised to the DGC company should it wish to extend, and in
1857 it entered into a new contract with the Bedford holdings to
extend its workings eastwards for another 924 fathoms along the

North portal of the Tavistock Canal tunnel. The date marks the start of its construction

The old basin of the Tavistock Canal above Morwellham. The water-wheel working the incline was behind the ivy-clad wall in front of the cottage

The bridge near Mill Hill, a clue to the old line of the 'cut' from the Tavistock Canal to Mill Hill quarries nearby. The other end of the bridge is now blocked

Granite milestone near Mill Hill

An early nineteenth-century granary at Mill Hill. A basin was excavated on the ground floor of the part projecting into the road where canal boats were moored for loading and unloading. The road in front was approximately the old line of the 'cut'

presumed line of the lode. It also undertook to deepen the engine shaft at Wheal Josiah to see if, as at Dolcoath, tin lay beneath the copper; while the Duke granted a right of way to build a railway line from the mine to Morwellham, and gave land for enlarging Morwellham dock provided the company undertook the work.

For the renewal of the lease and other concessions the Duke demanded £20,000, a 'fine' which sent a wave of shocked indignation through the metal-mining world. The Duke, however, was unmoved and the company paid up[6]. Few landlords have ever been in a more enviable position than was the Duke at this time. Through industrial ventures from which he personally recoiled, he was gaining a steadily mounting fortune at no risk to himself. Any land he leased was hedged around with burdensome safeguards for reinstatement. He contributed nothing to the mine, displayed no interest in it, and there is no certainty that he ever troubled to visit the workings. By 1857 over £100,000 in dues had showered into his lap—and he had even been paid £2,052 for the despoilation of the land.

Some of this wealth came back to Tavistock in the shape of a new market and town hall and an imposingly laid out square. Alleviation of a shocking housing shortage aggravated by the success of the mine was more grudgingly conceded: the Duke owned all the land from Tavistock to the Tamar and any building required his permission. By 1849 overcrowding had become so acute that the Portreeve of Tavistock sponsored a petition for the release of suitable sites for houses. The Duke's reply was to build 250 cottages at Tavistock, Gulworthy, Morwellham and on the mine itself. In appearance and layout they were models of their kind and were built for an overall cost of £22 each. The cottages each had four large rooms, one of which could easily be divided to make two bedrooms. Built between 1850 and 1860 they were let at rentals of from 1s 3d to 2s 6d a week, plus 1d a week each for a kitchen stove which the Duke replaced free when worn out. But good as they were there was

K

not half enough of them: in 1864 the Duke's agent was acknowledging that 'if 100 cottages were now ready to be disposed of in Tavistock they would all be occupied within a week by persons who really deserve and require them and the town would still be very overcrowded'.

THE MINE RAILWAY

The railway for which the company had been granted a right of way was urgently needed. It was costing the company 5s a ton to take ore to the river, and this in a year such as 1854 when 24,000 tons was taken to the quays amounted to £6,000.

Work on the new line began in 1857. It started at Wheal Anna Maria, where a coal yard and ore shoots or bins capable of holding 200 tons were built so that trucks could be loaded directly from them. The line, laid with 39-lb rails, ran for 300–400 yd along level ground, and then turned north in a loop to serve Wheal Emma, before resuming a southerly course which took it under the main road between Tavistock and Gunnislake. From there it followed the wooded hills bordering the Tamar to a point overlooking Morwellham, where a ½-mile long incline connected it to the port. Over a total length of 4½ miles the line's steepest gradient was 1 in 48. Its total cost was £12,595 all of which the company paid for out of capital.

The first train ran over the new railway in November 1859.[7] It was at first worked by a single locomotive, a second being added in 1859 and a third a year later. The first two locomotives had 12-in diameter cylinders and the third 7 in. They were in use twenty years before their boilers burnt out and were replaced by two 0-4-0 tank engines, built by John Spittle Ltd of Newport Mon, and named *Hugo* and *Ada*. Each had 10-in × 15-in stroke cylinders driving four 2-ft × 8-in coupled wheels, the boilers giving 90 lb working pressure, and wore a green livery picked out in yellow stripes. A fully laden train of eight wagons took twenty minutes to get from Wheal Maria to the head of the incline above Morwellham, where the $3\frac{1}{2}$-ton trucks were unhitched and attached to a wire rope wound around a drum powered by a 22-in stationary steam engine. The two descending trucks were balanced by two ascending, a double line of rails providing a passing point in the middle of the incline. A 25-ft diameter water-wheel connecting with a 'lift of pumps' drew water from the Tavistock Canal for the stationary engine and the locomotives. At the bottom of the incline the trucks ran out under a tunnel and on to rails carried on wooden staging above the quay. They had hinged bottoms for releasing the ore into piles on the tiled ore floors.

Although never used for passengers the line was well maintained, and a contemporary traveller on it thought it would add

> much to the enjoyment of excursionists up the Tamar if, leaving their steamers at Morwellham, they could complete the trip on the Devon Great Consols railway . . . it is just as well constructed as many a passenger line and judging from the ride over it in cushioned ore trucks equally as comfortable as a means of transport.

In its forty years of existence, only one serious mishap occurred: an elderly woman walking along the track failed to hear a train and was killed near Chimney Rock.

Materials and supplies were also carried for Collacombe, West Maria and Fortescue mines, which lay on the perimeter of the Devon Great Consols sett, while spur lines and inclines connected Wheal Emma and the saw mills of Wheal Josiah and the neighbouring Bedford United mine. In a full year the railway saved the company £4,000 in carriage charges, cutting the cost from 5s to 1s a ton—a rate also enjoyed by the Duke and his tenants. The provision of a new dock and larger ore-storage floors at Morwellham (see Chapter Two), reducing the need to use the quays at Newquay and Gawton, helped bring down the cost of returning 1 ton of ore by 5s 8d compared with 1858.

TAKING STOCK OF PROSPERITY

The company was now riding at the height of its prosperity. A new course of ore—the south lode—cut in 1858 was found to be rich for most of its 300 fathoms, forming particularly dense masses of ore rich in copper pyrites where it rejoined the main lode at Wheal Josiah. The mine was now the biggest single employer in the district, drawing its 1,230 workers not only from Tavistock but from Gunnislake, Calstock and Latchley. Among them were 168 girls and 217 boys; some of the children started work as early as eight years of age, picking over the ore and tending the buddles. Many had to walk 4 or 5 miles to work, and on winter mornings and evenings they could be seen trudging along the roads with their parents, holding lanterns lit by candles.

For some of them the company provided a school on the mine; in 1859—a year when dividends amounted to £45,050—the directors granted £100 for educational purposes. Parents were expected to contribute a small fee to help pay for 'an effective mistress'. The children took their meals separately, a room with a hot flue being provided for them to warm their feet in cold weather. Hot water for tea and coffee was always available, and each man had a lock-up cupboard.

Miners paid 1s 6d a month to a sick club to ensure medical attention for themselves and their families, with 4s a week, when ill. An injured man received £1 a month from the company 'as long as the amount is required', and dependents were assisted when a man was killed. Efforts were also made to prevent casualties. Iron tamping rods, the biggest single cause of explosion on mines because of their liability to give off sparks when struck, were prohibited and copper rods supplied in their place. Gunpowder was doled out in quantities sufficient only for immediate use. Visitors shown round would always carry away an impression of the workers' 'decent and orderly conduct'. The local maidens, singing hymns at their work, were regarded as examples to their counterparts in other mines who bore a reputation for strong language.

On the mine itself lived a self-contained community of nearly twenty mine agents and their families, for whom the company built a number of pleasant slate-fronted houses, some of which may still be seen. A brass band and choir formed on the mine gave concerts and glee evenings to help pass the long winter nights and the band gave at least one well-attended public concert. Any man with a good singing voice could always find employment on the mine, particularly if he was willing to join in a choir for singing hymns on Sunday.

The year 1865 was adopted as the Devon Great Consols twenty-first anniversary, and in May the directors paused to take stock of their vast undertaking. There was much to satisfy them. The deepest part of Wheal Josiah was now 220 fathoms, a man taking a full hour to climb to the surface. Four principal lodes were now being worked—the original main lode, the south lode (which branched from it and rejoined it at Wheal Josiah) the middle lode and the new south lode which was being worked mainly from the Railway Shaft at Wheal Emma. The water pumped from the mine was so poisonous that it nearly killed off the Tamar salmon fishery, and works had been set up to extract the copper it held in solution. The precipitate obtained fetched £48 a ton, compared with £5 5s a ton for 'common ore'.

The mine's surface works were spread over 140 acres, there were over 40 miles of levels and it was possible to walk uninterruptedly underground for $2\frac{1}{2}$ miles from Wheal Maria at the sett's western boundary to Wheal Emma at the extreme eastern end. The foundry maintained eight steam engines and thirty-three water-wheels, and was so complete in its resources that when a 40-in pumping engine had to be removed from Wheal Emma to Wheal Josiah it was dismantled, re-erected and working within thirteen days, without the help of outside labour.

Each month the mine consumed 200 tons of coal, 160 loads of timber (a load was 50 cu ft) and 33 cwt of gunpowder, while £1,200 a year was paid in rates and taxes to Tavistock parish. The wage bill was £3,200 and in the twenty-one years dividends little short of £1,000,000 had been paid to shareholders; the Duke of Bedford had received upwards of £210,000[8]. Anyone who in 1844 had spent £1 on a share had received in return £923 or an average of £44 11s a year. The yearly output over that period and the steady maintenance of dues and dividends is illustrated in the following table[9]:

	Copper ore sold			Amount realized, including carriage			Dues on ores			Dividends paid		
	Tons	cwt	qr	£	s	d	£	s	d	£	s	d
1845	382	1	2	4,313	19	5						
1846	13,292	10	2	116,068	15	0	8,321	15	6	72,704	0	0
1847	14,398	9	0	96,610	3	11	7,189	0	11	25,600	0	0
1848	14,413	6	3	102,933	7	7	7,881	9	5	15,204	16	4
1849	16,580	17	2	101,031	13	1	7,628	0	11	30,875	3	8
1850	15,431	18	0	104,554	18	6	7,906	5	9	34,304	0	0
1851	17,290	15	0	117,407	14	6	8,960	18	1	43,004	0	0
1852	18,964	18	0	118,334	2	0	9,027	3	3	39,936	0	0
1853	20,886	14	3	147,646	10	0	10,966	8	5	49,664	0	0
1854	24,378	19	2	153,837	0	2	12,117	1	4	64,512	0	0
1855	22,926	4	1	152,489	9	5	11,685	13	0	58,368	0	0
1856	23,922	19	2	140,843	11	9	10,769	19	4	56,320	0	0
1857	28,836	0	0	159,432	7	9	11,625	6	2	64,512	0	0
1858	25,172	13	3	138,356	15	1	11,376	16	2	61,440	0	0
1859	23,531	6	3	119,947	8	11	9,557	4	6	45,056	0	0
1860	22,839	2	1	115,285	8	7	9,287	11	7	48,128	0	0
1861	21,833	5	2	108,365	14	9	9,117	4	5	47,104	0	0
1862	20,855	6	2	103,330	0	4	8,521	6	3	44,032	0	0
1863	24,622	5	3	118,479	9	7	9,596	13	3	55,296	0	0
1864	26,834	7	2	130,175	7	8	10,503	10	11	56,320	0	0
1865	25,786	3	0	134,785	19	2	11,219	10	1	63,488	0	0

'The source of the prosperity of Tavistock is to be found not so much in the mining operations of the locality as in the extraordinary success of one great concern—Devon Great Consols,' it was noted at the time and the mine in fact gave indirect employment and security to over 6,000 people in an area which included not only Tavistock, but Calstock, Gunnislake and Latchley.

In celebration the directors provided a monster dinner for every man, woman and child on the mine. Accommodation for nearly 1,200 diners was provided in wooden sheds on the mine. The fare provided included 1 ton of roast and boiled beef, 1,300 lb of bread, eight hogsheads of beer, four of cider and one of lemonade, the latter brewed on the mine. The only speech was from Captain Isaac Richards who told his guests that in the twenty-one years the mine had been working 420,000 tons of ore had been raised and sold and the 'exploration of the underground had travelled 25 miles'.

DECLINE AND ARSENIC

The boll weevil (*Anthonomus grandis*) is the most serious pest of cotton in the United States; even today it causes an annual loss of more than one-tenth of the entire cotton crop. It is controlled by spraying with calcium arsenate and as it began to spread more and more rapidly through the cotton plantations of Texas, Oklahoma Arkansas and half a dozen other states in the 1870s and 80s the demand for arsenical pesticides grew increasingly. This was one of the biggest factors in prolonging the existence of Devon Great Consols mine into the last thirty years of the nineteenth century. For by 1870 half the world's supply of arsenic was coming from the walls of the failing copper lodes of Blanchdown.

The directors and miners who feasted in the open air on boiled beef and beer in June 1865 had probably little inkling of the important part the disregarded arsenical ores abounding in the workings would play in their future. Yet in the deeper levels of the sett there were already significant signs that the copper lodes were dwindling.

By 1868, after twenty years of intensive working, the great main lode which in places had been 40 ft or more thick was nearly exhausted of ore. At Wheal Fanny and Wheal Maria the reserves were rapidly diminishing, while the south lode at Wheal Josiah which had yielded nearly £600,000 was ending in barren ground at 144 fathoms[10].

The directors, when renewing their lease in 1857, had set great store on obtaining the land east of Wheal Emma, where geological indications led to the hope that the rich main lode would continue. But a level driven a full mile from the eastern shaft at Wheal Emma failed to produce a single ton of ore and from this setback dates the gradual decline of the mine's prosperity.

The growing exhaustion of the lodes coincided with a marked fall in the price of copper which led to less ore being raised. In 1872 only 16,392 tons of ore had been brought to surface compared with 27,000 tons ten years earlier. By this time the Devon and Cornwall copper mines were rapidly losing their pre-eminence to the mines of the United States and Australia. Out of a total world production of 900,000 tons of copper between 1861 and 1870, the United Kingdom (where Devon Great Consols was the chief mine) had produced 142,000 tons. But in the next decade this had fallen to 47,000 tons out of a world production of 1,189,400 tons. Germany was producing more copper than Devon and Cornwall.

In turning to arsenic production to bolster the falling receipts, the company sought to utilize its large dumps of low-grade ore as well as the 'mundic' or mispickel left standing on the walls of the lodes after the copper had been extracted. This was in places nearly 5 ft thick and contained 30 per cent of arsenic. Arsenic by this time had many uses in the chemical industries and in the manufacture of glass and enamel as well as in insecticides; it was widely prescribed in medicines for its tonic properties, and a curious and widespread sect in Austria even made a habit of eating it in the belief that they would live longer. It was an important constituent in paints and dyes, and as copper arsenate it was used to fix pigments in fabrics and wall papers. (After a number of deaths through people inadvertently licking their fingers after touching arsenic crystals on the wallpaper, its use for this purpose was abandoned.)

To obtain arsenic the ore was washed and broken into pieces small enough to pass through a $\frac{1}{2}$-in sieve. It was then roasted in calciners, of which there were two types on the mine. The earlier or Brunton calciner was a dome-shaped structure with a circular bed of bricks laid on an iron plate underneath which was a furnace. The brick bed and plate were kept revolving by a water-wheel, and as they turned a series of obliquely set teeth gradually stirred the ore until it was completely roasted. Another type of calciner in more general use was the Oxland cylinder, a 50-ft long wrought iron tube lined with firebricks, mounted at a slight angle and rotated like a spit on rollers. The ore was shovelled in at the top and the rotary motion of the tube gradually worked it down to the furnace, where the sulphur content of the ore aided its combustion.

From both types of furnace the arsenic vapour from the roasting ore, yellow in colour and smelling faintly of garlic, was discharged through regulating dampers into a series of flues whose masonry walls were $2\frac{1}{2}$ ft thick[11]. These in turn connected with a labyrinth of brick chambers on whose walls and floors the vapour condensed into grey crystals. From these chambers another run of flues took the surplus vapour over limestone screens to extract as much of the residual arsenic and sulphur as possible, and on to a stack, usually built on high ground to avoid the fumes blighting the surrounding vegetation.

After the first burning the arsenic was little more than 80 per cent pure and had to be further treated in a refining furnace heated by a smokeless fuel made up of anthracite and coke. The vapour passed into a further series of brick chambers with clean tiled floors, where it cooled into deposits of pure white crystals. These had to be dug and shovelled out by hand. The men doing this wore mouth masks and ear plugs and muffled their feet and ankles in sacks to avoid 'arsenic sores' caused by the strongly caustic crystals. To ensure cleanliness two changing rooms were provided for the workers.

In the last process the crystals were ground between two granite millstones into a powder as fine as flour and then packed for market in 4-cwt casks lined with blue paper. The finished product was 99·5 per cent pure white arsenic and one-sixth of a teaspoonful was judged sufficient to kill a person.

By 1868, two years after its production had begun on the mine, 473 tons of arsenic had been sold and contracts entered into to supply another 150 tons a month for twelve months, at a price of £6 a ton delivered to Morwellham or Gawton quays. The Wheal Maria arsenic works were then the largest in Devon and Cornwall, consisting of five calcining furnaces, three refining furnaces and 4,645 ft of flues. By the summer of 1869 production had been stepped up to 160 tons a month—half the world's arsenic supply. Sales of refined arsenic were by 1871 making up 20 per cent of the mine's receipts. The arsenic works were successively enlarged until they finally covered 8 acres and were capable of producing 3,500 tons a month, with seven calciners and 5,429 ft of flues. A steam engine powered the arsenic-grinding mill and the casks were made in the mine's cooperages at Blanchdown and Morwellham.

DISPUTES AND LOCK OUTS

The high dividends received for over twenty-five years by the Devon Great Consols shareholders were not reflected in the wages of the miners, nor were the psalm-singing bal maidens whose devotion to their work so impressed visitors a true reflection of the relationship between management and employees.

The average wage at Devon Great Consols was £3 12s for a five-week month or about 14s a week. For men on the dressing floors the wage was £3 5s; dividers, weighers and shippers at Morwellham received £4 10s a five-week month, through working longer hours. The bal maidens, whose job was breaking the ore into small pieces with long-handled hammers, received 1s to 1s 3d a day. This was rough, muscular work, but an observer in 1864 thought it could not be regarded as injurious because 'all looked the picture of health'.

Such wages provided little more than a bare living and were often overtaken by rising prices. Many miners had large families, a not untypical example being Charles Masters, who was killed at Wheal Fortescue near Lamerton, leaving behind a wife and eleven children. As the Rector of Sydenham observed in an appeal for money for the bereaved dependants, 'with a large family and scant earnings, to live had been for him for some time past a problem difficult of solution'.

By August 1867 real wages throughout the area had been reduced by 50 per cent, mainly through the increased price of provisions. Loaves made from barley flour were a substitute in many families for wheaten bread; even the coarse 'seconds' loaf supplied to the poor-law institutions was beyond the reach of many. Dripping was largely used in place of butter, and pork replaced beef and mutton, many miners keeping a pig.

As early as 1850 there had been a strike by 200 pickers for more wages; when they returned after staying out for a day they were told their services were no longer required. But a far more spectacular dispute arose in 1866.

A long-standing grievance in the area was the growing custom of diluting skilled mining labour with agricultural workers and other inexperienced men who slowed a skilled man's work on the tribute pitches. (In tribute work, the more a miner sent to the surface the more he received when the ore was sold.) This practice contributed to the founding in East Cornwall in 1865 of the Miner's Mutual Benefit Association, one of whose rules stipulated that in the larger mines a committee of miners should decide whether, with the labour

available, a fair price had been allowed by the agent for the working
of a 'pitch'. Mánagers and agents reacted violently to this attempt
to dictate wages, and any known Association members were
victimized by being locked out.

On 26 February 1866 some locked-out miners seized a blackleg
worker as he came up from his shift at Drakewalls, put him astride
a fir pole and ran him smartly through Gunnislake amid great cheer-
ing and shouts of 'blackleg'. The frightened manager of Drakewalls
armed himself with a large knife—which was only wrested from him
with difficulty—and appealed to the police. In Tavistock, where
many miners were members of the Association, the news of this
escapade aroused strong feelings, especially when the Callington
magistrates sent the Drakewalls men to prison. Rumours spread of
thousands of workmen coming up from the Caradon and Liskeard
mines to assist the Tavistock and Gunnislake miners. Devon Great
Consols, with the largest labour force in the district, became a focal
point of discontent. Threatening anonymous letters were sent to the
agents and mine captains. *The Western Daily Mercury's* special cor-
respondent noted that 'It is a most notorious fact that the underground miners openly insult the mine captains and attempt to force
the men to belong to the Miner's Association.' Out of fear for their
safety and that of the mine property the agents appealed to the
Tavistock magistrates, who telegraphed to the chief constable of
Exeter. He arranged for 150 constables drawn from all parts of the
country to be sent to the mine.

Friday, 2 March was a day of particular tension. The men became
more and more threatening and there was some danger that the
pumps would be stopped. The magistrates in a fit of panic appealed
to the commander-in-chief at Plymouth for troops. On the following
day a special train brought 150 men of the 66th Regiment to Tavistock; they were held in reserve at the Bedford Hotel. On the mine
itself were 130 members of the regular constabulary, to be aug-
mented by 150 special constables sworn in for the occasion.

The scene on Saturday when the sale of pitches for underground working began lived long in local memory. Over 2,000 people stood around Count House where the 'pitch bargains' were auctioned, among them 300 policemen drawn up in three divisions ready for any clash with angry miners. The sale of 'bargains' began and ended in almost total silence. So general was the agreement that the price offered was too low to ensure fair wages that only four of the twenty-four 'bargains' offered were taken up. At this rate work on the mine would cease and pumping stop. An appeal to the sullen and silent groups of miners by the resident director W. A. Thomas 'to go to work like men' ended in a shouting dialogue in which he got the worst of the exchanges. Faced with what seemed a solid front Thomas left the scene with a promise that the pitches would be kept open until Monday.

The stand of the Devon Great Consols men was widely looked on as a test case by other miners. This was particularly true at Hingston Down mine, just beyond Gunnislake, where Captain Richard Richards, a diehard opponent of the men's demands, had received a threatening anonymous letter. A detachment of the 65th Foot was towed up in launches by a Government steamer to Cotehele Quay where they waited with boxes of ball cartridges ready to march.

But there were too many hungry and unemployed miners from West Cornwall looking for work for the strike to be successful. As the mine management brought them in, the firm front of the 'Association men' began to crumble, and by the end of March most of them had gone back to work, though about seventy Devon policemen remained a few days longer billeted at Blanchdown, 'very pleased with the sumptuous fare provided each day for them by the proprietors of the mine'. The Association collapsed and a secondary demand for £4, or 18s a week, for a five-week month was whittled down to £3 5s for a four-week month.

The principle of the five-week month proved a hard one for the company to relinquish, and with falling dividends and uncertain sales the directors tried to reintroduce it in 1878. But the miners, seeing in it a proposal whereby they lost four weeks' pay each year, were solidly against it. Unlike 1866, this time their strike had a good deal of local support, the Portreeve of Tavistock opening a fund for their relief. Again after a stubborn trial of strength a compromise was reached, the men agreeing to a cut in wages from 14s 9d to 13s 7d a week providing the company did not introduce the five-week month. The church bells of Tavistock were rung in celebration, but the men were not so successful in March 1879 when they stopped work in protest against the directors' decision to cut all wages by 10 per cent. It was now claimed that the mine was losing £5,000 a year; this time the management refused to budge, and the men, after remaining idle until mid-April, went back on the company's terms.

THE LOST TIN LODES

The company had also been wrestling with other difficulties. It had shared with every other major mining concern in Devon and Cornwall the dream of emulating Dolcoath mine at Camborne, where—in a similar geological situation—rich deposits of tin had been found underneath the exhausted copper lodes. Shareholders were restive about their falling dividends, and to provide the £30,000 necessary to explore Richards's shaft at Wheal Josiah for tin, in 1872 a major financial reconstruction was undertaken for the first time since the company had been founded. It now became a limited liability undertaking, with a capital of £51,200 in 10,200 shares of £5 each of which only £2 was called up.*

To prove the ground Richards's shaft, which was closest to the granite, was to be deepened to 300 fathoms, and the terms of the

---

* Collins's *London and Westcountry Chamber of Mines, 1901–03.* The total amount of capital called up from first to last was less than £30,000.

Duke's lease required that levels should be driven north, east and west. By 1875 the shaft was being sunk through hard ground at the rate of 10 fathoms a month. The men could work only for short spells because of ventilation difficulties (this was the deepest shaft on the mine) and a jet of cold water was thrown down the shaft to reduce the temperature. Even then, the ventilation allowed the exploration of only 400 yd at the bottom of the shaft out of an area of 1 square mile. No trace of tin was found.

A decision was taken to explore farther in the adjoining Wheal Emma sett. Although the bulk of the copper from the mine was now coming from Wheal Emma, tin stones were found there in 1882. On the advice of the renowned Captain Josiah Thomas of Dolcoath, work was concentrated on the Railway shaft at Wheal Emma, which was already 205 fathoms deep. Rock drills, which along with other gear cost the company £5,000, speeded progress, and at a cost of £18 a fathom three years later sufficient tin had been raised to sell for £115. But no worthwhile deposits were found, and at 260 fathoms the exploration was abandoned. Sixteen years of almost continuous costly effort had led to little more than the discovery of 2 tons of tin stone[12].

DISSENSION AND CLOSURE

The mine now had little more than fifteen years of active life left and these were to be lived out in a gathering twilight of declining sales, financial crises and boardroom dissensions centring on the new chairman and managing director, Peter Watson. A self-made man, he differed from most of the other directors in having had practical experience in metalliferous mining, some of it gained in his early days in the Tavistock district. Appointed to the board in 1877 he was a bluff personality with the appearance of a jovial John Bull, who would delight his hearers by his lucid explanations of the mine's workings and its problems. His confident manner and easy charm won friends, but an influential minority thought him too autocratic and disliked his rather dictatorial methods.

When he took the chair at the half-yearly meeting in 1880 there were still hopes that tin might be found, and the mine seemed to be entering another period of prosperity. A new course of ore had been found in Watson's Mine, in the southern end of the sett where work had been suspended in 1850 when the rest of the mine was still so rich that it was not worth bothering about; it was now proposed to drain it by connecting 280 fathoms of flat rods with the water-wheel at Richards's shaft. During the previous six months over 5,000 tons of ore had been sold for £14,000, a rate of £2 14s a ton—although in 1857 it had fetched £6 a ton. A contract worth £30,000 had been signed for arsenic, and the company for the previous six months had realized a record £15,517 in arsenic sales. Thirteen shafts were in use, and there were now over 5½ miles of underground tramway. The company also had man engines at Wheal Josiah and Wheal Emma and new condensers were being built for the arsenic reduction works.

Labour relations had also greatly improved. 'The wages paid to the miners are better,' said the chairman, 'and we have recently volunteered to give them four holidays in the year, on Easter Monday, Whit Monday, Midsummer Day and Christmas Day.' A dividend of £1 12s a share was declared for 1880. The directors also had their fees increased by 100 gns to 500 gns and Watson's remuneration was doubled to £500 a year[13].

But then a savage winter in the early months of 1881 froze the Tamar, immobilized the mine water-wheels and prevented sales of arsenic, now the lifeblood of the company. In May 1881 the copper standard dropped to the lowest in the history of the mine. In 1884 fifty men had to be discharged, while the remainder had their wages reduced. The Duke was persuaded in 1885 to forego £1,000 of his dues, and he eventually agreed a year later to remit all of them until

Group of miners, circa 1880. The site is probably the old Lady Bertha mine near Tavistock

172

Wheal Martha and New Consols, Luckett. The result of over a century of working for tin, copper and arsenic

Okel Tor mine on a bend in the Tamar above Calstock. The workings of Gawton mine can be seen on the right bank

the mine paid dividends again.* He was getting more and more difficult to deal with and wanted his pheasant coverts back.

The company for its part levied a further 10s a share to work the mine more vigorously, and from 1891–6 earned a profit of £13,500. The labour force was now under 400 but the mine was still the largest single employer in the area. Although water had long been allowed to rise in the lower levels to save pumping costs, Wheal Maria and Wheal Josiah were still sending ore from the 157-fathoms level, and Wheal Emma from 162 fathoms. Some of the stopes gave as much as 19 tons of mundic and 1 ton of copper ore per fathom, while the measured reserves were stated to be over 9,471 tons.

At a meeting in London in June 1901 when a loss of nearly £3,000 in two years had been blamed on the price of iron, steel, coal and coke, the smouldering enmity between one of the shareholders and the chairman burst into flames. Watson was accused of withholding information and thwarting inquiries about the mine's future—a charge he strongly denied. More revealing was a plea by J. H. Collins, a well-known personality in West of England mining circles, that the directors 'might consider the question of adopting some more modern system of electrical machinery throughout the mine which, driven by the Tamar, would end stoppages caused through there being too much or too little water'.

Many still found it impossible to believe that so rich a mine should now be tottering to its end. Sales of arsenic worth £25,504 and of copper worth £2,737 in 1900 led Captain Clemo, junr, to claim 'with honesty' that the mine was looking better than for some time past; Moses Bawden, the purser, who lived at a rental of £1 a week in Tamar View, a spacious mine house overlooking the Tavistock–Gunnislake road at Gulworthy, estimated it had another 6,587 tons of arsenical mundic and 1,854 tons of copper. 'And,' he said, 'in taking away the arsenical mundic we might discover more.'

---

* From 1881–6 the Duke received £10,000 in royalties, although the mine had not paid any dividends.

L

But the price of arsenic was now slumping to £10 a ton, and it was proving almost impossible to sell. The board, which had already borrowed to the limit, was unable to raise money to meet immediate debts or continue operations. A circular asking the shareholders to provide further capital found only 440 willing to subscribe; 9,482 did not want to and others did not bother to reply. A dividend of 2s 6d a share paid in 1899 proved to be the last. The working expenses of the mine were now something like £1,500 a month, and since 1900 it had incurred a loss of £100 a week. The Duke was not willing to renew the lease.

Throughout 1901 the mine was more or less moribund. Its imminent closure created anxiety not only in Tavistock but in Calstock and Gunnislake, where many employees who were relatively old men faced a bleak Christmas and workless winter. An expected contract for arsenic did not materialize, and on Saturday, 30 November 1901 all work stopped except for pumping and the company went into voluntary liquidation. Moses Bawden, who was ill in bed when the news was brought to him, turned his face to the wall and burst into tears.

The closure affected 351 employees, but while pumping continued there remained hope that the mine would reopen if the price of arsenic rose. The lode at the bottom of Watson's mine was still capable of yielding 6 tons of mundic and copper a fathom and the underground workings 'had not looked so well for years'. In a last effort Peter Watson called in Captain W. H. Borlase, whose report bore out this optimism. He estimated the value of the ore in sight at £57,000, and recommended a better application of the enormous water power available and the provision of cage roads in the shafts.

But the value of Captain Borlase's advice was never tested. The long-standing feud between one of the chief shareholders and the chairman could no longer be contained. In June 1902, after nearly sixty years of active life, the richest and most remarkable example of Victorian mining enterprise in the South West of England stumbled and sank to a furtive end amid the whimpers of a board-room wrangle.

Those who a year earlier had been displaced were guaranteed employment by the Duke for the rest of the winter on his estates, and to some who had been working for forty years on the mine he gave a pension. There were not many of them, and out of royalties amounting to over £250,000 the Duke could no doubt afford the money, but taken together the two gestures remain the biggest single act of charity of any soil landlord in the history of Devon and Cornish mining. Even so the Tavistock poor rate went up by 1d and it was reported there were fifty summonses in preparation against people unable to pay their rates.

With almost indecent haste the mine materials were sold off in 1903. The Duke, anxious to restore his ravished plantations, had most of the shafts filled and the bulk of the surface building levelled so completely that only the scantiest evidence remained to be recorded on the 1907 Ordnance Survey map of what had once been the biggest copper mine in Europe. The railway was dismantled[14], Morwellham reverted to the Duke's ownership, and the hundreds of tons of scrap metal on the site found ready purchasers among the Germans who, it is still asserted in Tavistock, fired it back in guns and shells in the first world war.

In its fifty-five years, the mine made the following returns:

Ore sold[15]					Value		
	21 cwt	cwt	qr		£	s	d
	736,229	1	1		3,473,046	6	0
Dues on ores sold:	£264,210						
Less remitted	£2,623						
					261,587	0	0

Refined arsenic sold:							
	tons	cwt	qr	lb			
	72,279	3	0	11	625,062	4	0
Dues	£26,967	10	7				
Less remitted	£7,662	2	4				
					19,305	8	3

Mines' costs, from commencement to 9–16 March 1901   2,052,206 6 9
Other payments, steam engines, water-wheels, railway,
          reduction works, etc   658,336 13 0
Dividends (162) paid or £119 13 0 per share   1,225,216 0 0

	2I cwt	*cwt*	*qr*	*lb*		£	*s*	*d*		£	*s*	*d*
Tin stuff sold	64	12	0	0	@	2	5	0		145	5	8
Black tin sold	64	10	0	22	@	8	7	6		24	13	3
Lead ore sold	64	13	0	0	@	6	2	6		3	19	7

All of this had been produced from 140 acres of ground, twelve
main shafts and 45 miles of underground levels. When the mine
stopped in 1901 the twenty points being worked were yielding 214
tons of arsenical pyrites and copper ore—an average of nearly 11
tons a fathom. To produce the 72,279 tons of arsenic over 600,000
tons of arsenical pyrites had been calcined.

SUBSEQUENT HISTORY

Some intermittent working, mainly sponsored by the Duke of
Bedford, continued on the mine until 1940. Arsenic was recovered
from above the water level at Wheal Maria and Wheal Fanny, where
the main lode was 6 ft thick yielding 5 per cent of pure arsenic. A
slump in the price caused work to be finally abandoned in 1925,
although almost as much mundic still remains underground in the
mine as was ever extracted. A legacy of this latter arsenic working
is the tall chimney put up in 1922 which can be seen clearly from
the main road approaching Gulworthy from Tavistock. This connected with a new refinery put up at about the same time, while a
2-ft gauge light railway about 2 miles long was built to transport
small amounts of tin and wolfram from Wheal Frementor to a
crushing plant at Bedford United mines.

The production of copper precipitate carried on for a few years
longer. This was mainly at the so-called Higher and Lower Copper
Works on the banks of the Tamar, where the burrows of Wheal

Fanny were treated. Extensive traces of this work can be found today in the form of thousands of horse shoes (used for precipitating the copper) which lie scattered over the ground, as well as the remains of wooden launders and treatment ponds. About 20 tons of copper precipitate a year was obtained, earning from 1914–18 over £11,000. Work seems to have stopped finally in 1940 after being brought to a standstill by drought. The last mineral material to be obtained from Devon Great Consols was probably a quantity of ochre for paint manufacture, obtained during the last war from the mine's main drainage adit.

It is a strange experience to walk over the site of Devon Great Consols mine today. Except for the vast heaps of calcined waste and the skeletal remains of the arsenic reduction works built after the first world war, almost all the surface features have vanished. The course of the main lode eastwards from Wheal Maria can be followed from the evidence of surface disturbance, but foundry, engine houses and water-wheels have vanished, and most of the arsenic flues and refining chambers pillaged for their bricks. But one can still walk by the course of the Great Leat almost to its source at the now-demolished weir near Latchley, and it is still possible to follow the greater part of the course of the mine's railway. On the spot where the stationary winding engine stood, at the top of the incline above Morwellham, burrowing rabbits turn out coal and ashes dumped from the long-dead boiler fires. Above Blanchdown farm the outlines of the pits which housed the great 40-ft water-wheels and the inclines up which the power rods travelled can still be made out with the aid of patience and a map.

CHAPTER NINE

The East Cornwall Mineral Railway

ON Monday, 16 November 1863 a band of people assembled in a meadow near Calstock, close to the site of the now-derelict incline station of the East Cornwall Mineral Railway. Near them a group of workmen ceremoniously held their spades in the form of a crescent. The owner of the field, Thomas Bowhay, who lived nearby at Albaston, drove a spade into the short turf, cut out a square and trundled it away in a wheelbarrow. Other turves were cut by a Callington solicitor and by the agent for the Duchy of Cornwall. The whole proceedings took about a quarter of an hour and 'terminated in a round of cheers'[1]. Thus began an enterprise which nine years and four Acts of Parliament later was to blossom into the East Cornwall Mineral Railway—a railway which has existed with modifications and change of gauge into the age of diesel traction.

THE NEEDS OF 'A BARREN DISTRICT'

As with the Tavistock Canal nearly sixty years earlier, the East Cornwall Mineral Railway was called into being to solve a growing transport problem. Between Calstock and Callington in the late 1850s some seventeen mines were actively at work, as well as granite quarries, brick, tile and fireclay works, at least one paper mill, a foundry and fertilizer works. Farming produce from a wide area had to be carried to the Tamar to be sent down to Plymouth, and there was a growing market-garden industry in an area increasingly recognized as being as favourable as Penzance for the growth of early crops.

178

All had to be served by an immense horse traffic using a network of poor roads and steep hills to the river quays at Calstock (Chapter Two), where ores were weighed, sampled and arranged for shipment to the South Wales smelting works and from where coal, timber, lime and manures were carried inland. This primitive, expensive carriage had long been recognized as a brake on progress. In modern values it cost 6s a ton a mile to bring ore by horse and cart to Calstock's quays, and when the railway was projected one firm estimated it would save £600 a year (about £3,600 today) on the cost of carriage.

A powerful secondary reason for the promotion of the line was anger and exasperation with the South Devon Railway for leaving Callington out of the route of its projected Launceston branch. Thomas Woollcombe, chairman of the South Devon Railway, in 1860 had described the North Cornwall area as a barren district and an unrewarding field for railway enterprise[2]. History was to prove him right, but at a time when the air was full of rumours of railway development and of plans for linking up the old-established Bodmin & Wadebridge Railway with Okehampton and Truro, the summary dismissal of an important industrial enclave in East Cornwall caused immense resentment and bitterness. In effect it became a challenge to the district to promote its own line, a challenge taken up by Edward Nicolls, a Callington solicitor and steward of the manor of Calstock, who began negotiations with a number of mine adventurers in London to raise capital. Over a period of years Nicolls was the brain and mainspring behind a succession of efforts to link Callington, Gunnislake and Calstock to a main-line railway, and although he was to be dead many years before the area had its own passenger-train service he deserves remembrance as a pioneer of railway development in the Tamar Valley.

THE TAMAR, KIT HILL & CALLINGTON SCHEME

In January 1859 the Tamar Coal, Manure & General Mercantile Company was formed—with, it was stressed, a 'respectable directorate'. The company had an extensive barge trade on the Tamar with headquarters at Kelly Quay, Calstock, where wharves, an engine works, stores and lime kilns ran along a continuous length of 1,359 ft of quays. The company immediately launched plans to build an incline plane from the quay up the Danescombe valley to a point 350 ft above Calstock, and the hope was expressed (significantly in view of later events) that 'this might eventually extend to Kelly Bray'[3]. The rope-worked incline 36 chains long and with a slope of 1 in 6 was well established by the middle of 1860. Plans for its extension were rapidly pushed ahead and under Nicolls's guidance the Tamar, Kit Hill & Callington Railway was incorporated in 1862, with capital of £60,000 in 6,000 shares. Two years later (29 July 1864) it was re-incorporated as a statutory company and the capital increased to £70,000.

'The inhabitants of Callington are going to have a railway after all,' announced *The Western Morning News*. 'The matter has been kept very quiet and many are surprised that preparations are so far advanced.' Although the object of the line was principally 'the facilitation of traffic, passenger trains will also be run'. The *Mining Journal* with more enthusiasm than accuracy announced that all the shares had been taken up and were at a premium; Nicolls had this denied at a public meeting at Callington[4]. Almost all the money 'had come from London' and the tardiness of local support was to lead to difficulties.

The line was to begin 'in a portion of Calstock in a piece of land adjoining the river' and to terminate at Callington. Not only was it hoped to capture the mining and quarrying trade in East Cornwall but a considerable 'exit trade' was anticipated from the mines on the Devon bank of the Tamar above Gunnislake.

By August 1864, although the Bill had only just passed the Lords and Commons, 'two-thirds of the railway is ready for laying of the permanent way, three-fourths of the proposed line is purchased and a thousand tons of rails are on the ground waiting to be laid by hundreds of workmen who are at work on the undertaking'. In fact some 2½ miles of line were ready to take the permanent way, 600 tons of rails had been delivered on the line and 100 additional workmen were ready. On this basis it seemed likely that in 'six months time the Callington mines will be sending their ores by railway to the sampling quays on the Tamar to be shipped in barges which come alongside from the steamers which touch Kelly wharf'. There was talk of extending the line southwards from Callington to Saltash and of uniting Callington with the Launceston, Bodmin & Wadebridge Railway by 'an extension northward which may possibly be produced to Bude Haven on the north coast'[5].

But local people who had paid lip service to the project were reluctant to invest any money in it. Many thought the line was being built too cheaply (it was costing less than £9,000 a mile), and although the South Wales contractor to prove his good faith offered to take two-thirds of his payment in shares, his insistence that despite the hilly country 'there was no engineering difficulties' caused some surprise.

By the end of September the doubts had proved only too well founded. The contractor, despite his earlier confidence, found himself in money difficulties. At the end of the year work was at a standstill, the company 'becoming involved in difficulties from which they could not be extricated after several thousands had been spent in obtaining the Act, purchasing the land, cutting the line and building bridges'[6]. Shortly afterwards time for the compulsory purchase of the land expired and the whole scheme was abandoned. Track and works lay dormant, although it is possible that a portion of the line as far as Gunnislake Clitters mine was used[7].

THE RAILWAY ACHIEVED

For four years the works lay crumbling. During this time the South Devon Railway had reached Launceston via Lydford (1 July 1865), by means of a subsidiary company, the Launceston & South Devon Railway, which began carrying freight on 21 August 1865. This emphasized all the more the isolation of the Callington–Calstock area. Nicolls, frustrated by indifference, rebuffed by landowners and mocked by the crumbling cuttings and rusting rails, for six years ceaselessly cast back and forth to convince the district that if it were ever to have a railway it must itself provide it. In 1869 the scheme was revived, as the Callington–Calstock Railway, with this time a firm promise of 50,000 tons of traffic a year. The new company, with a capital of £60,000 and powers to borrow up to a further £20,000, was authorized by its Act of 9 August 1869 to construct just under 8 miles of 3 ft 6 in gauge track between the two places named in its title. Two years later this was changed to the East Cornwall Mineral Railway; under this style it was completed and quietly with no ceremony, opened to goods traffic on 7 May 1872, serving a population estimated at 7,500. The line in fact never reached Callington; its terminus at Kelly Bray, close to a gaping mineshaft, was nearly a mile away, up a wide and hilly road open to all the winds from Hingston Down. Variously named Kelly Bray, Callington Road and now simply Callington it has remained there to this day.

The new line went earnestly about its business, one of the first freights carried being a truckload of coals for Callington gasworks chartered by James Venning, a future Portreeve of Callington and on whom Nicolls's mantle as pioneer of railway schemes for the area was shortly to fall. It was worked from the incline station to the Kelly Bray terminus by two squat tall-funnelled engines in the plainest of plain liveries which strutted like ducklings up and down a track through the hilly and often treeless stretch of countryside where nature had hidden much of her wealth underground. Its rope-worked incline 35 chains long (horses pulled the trucks along the wharves) used the counterbalance principle with the assistance of a stationary engine at the top. Two loaded 6-ton wagons were drawn up as three were let down, a passing loop being provided in the middle.

This incline was probably the most interesting feature of the line. Clear rules were drawn up for the guidance of the signal boy who manned the halfway loop. He must

> pay particular attention to the wire rope, pulleys, rollers, points, etc., and waggons passing up or down and, should anything go wrong, he must immediately signify the same by putting his Semaphore Signal at danger and by raising and violently waving his Red flag to the Signalman at the top of the incline, who in his turn, will, in the same manner as last described, signal to the engineman to stop hauling. Should these signals by any means be unobserved attention will be attracted by shouting or any other available method.[8]

The semaphore signal was sited on the west side of the line just above the upper end of the loop. A curvature prevented this being seen from the quay. The incline was not worked during darkness, fog or snow.

The station at the top of the incline included a small marshalling yard, wagon-repair shed, water tower and winding-engine house. Some of the buildings still exist and, together with the surface remains of Calstock Consols mine a stone's throw away, form a compact if sad reminder of vanished industrial enterprise.

From the incline station the line ran under the main Calstock road, around Drakewalls mine to Gunnislake, crossing the main road by a bridge at the top of Sand Hill. At the Gunnislake depot were private branches or sidings to Greenhill arsenic works, Clitters mine and Pearson's quarry. The line then curled along the northern flank of Hingston Down, where goods depots were established at Cox's Park (now Latchley station) and Monk's Corner (for Luckett

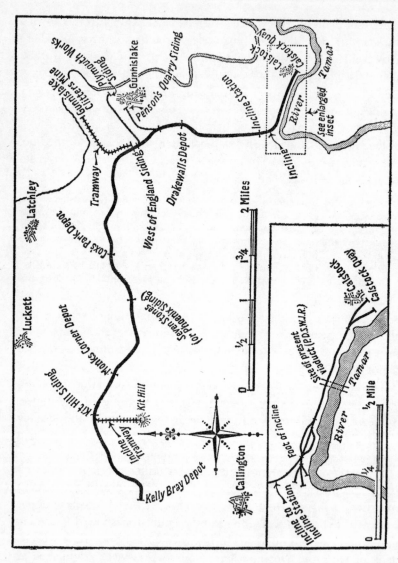

East Cornwall Mineral Railway showing its relation to Calstock Quay

village and New Consols mine). This was the highest point on the railway. Shortly before the terminus at Kelly Bray was Downgate siding, where a long inclined plane served Kit Hill quarry; while at Kelly Bray terminus other sidings were put down for the loading of ore from Kit Hill, Holmbush and Redmoor mines. The whole route had seven level crossings, four of which were manned. Except for one short, sharp fall the gradient was almost wholly against the engine, the Kelly terminus being 640 ft above sea level.

The two saddle-tank engines were of a standard 0-4-0 type built in 1871 by Neilson & Co of Glasgow. They had 3 ft 1 in wheels and 10 in × 12 in outside cylinders; the boiler—10 ft long—developed a working pressure of 90 lb. With a total weight in working order of 13 tons, they closely resembled those the company supplied to the Redruth & Chasewater Railway. Built for short hauls and low speeds they gave extraordinarily reliable service even if, at times, they could not take the steep inclines when heavily loaded. The usual working practice was to take six wagons to Monks Corner and go back for the remainder. The whole train was then coupled up and would 'make a rush down the decline and up the next incline to the terminus'. Signalling was rudimentary, a traveller on the line in 1893 noting some semaphore signals 'which appeared more for ornament than use'[9]. The company's first half-dozen wagons were hand-built by a Calstock carpenter, A. W. Williams, in the wagon shed at the top of the incline.

Comparative prosperity smiled on the line in its first four years. The half-year ending 30 June 1876, for example, produced a profit of £1,140, mainly from the coal, ore and arsenic trade. The mundic ore from which arsenic was obtained abounded in the mines in the neighbourhood, and in addition to the Devon Great Consols works there were arsenic refining plants at Coombe, near Harrowbarrow, and at Greenhill, adjoining Gunnislake Clitters mine, to which sidings led from the railway. The directors began to revive old dreams of expansion into a passenger service.

One plan was to convert the line to standard gauge with a viaduct over the Tamar at Gawton from which a line would run to Morwellham Quay and another to the South Devon system at Tavistock. An Act was eventually obtained in 1876 authorizing the construction of an additional $8\frac{1}{3}$ miles, planned as a separate undertaking. But depression hit the mines again; many closed and the scheme was abandoned in July 1879.

These periodic depressions were to plague the undertaking much as they had plagued the Tavistock Canal. Although few admitted it openly, the great days of copper mining in Devon and Cornwall were now over. Some of the mines of the district, like Wheal Williams at Latchley, Wheal Tom and Lammoerhooe Wheal Maria [*sic*] on the Devon side of the Tamar, which were mentioned as producers in the railway's original prospectus were now little more than half-remembered names. The enigmatic Drakewalls started and stopped with monotonous frequency: in five years between 1874 and 1880 its production of black tin had dropped from 224 tons to $1\frac{1}{4}$ tons. The line's best customer was Gunnislake Clitters (see Chapter Ten), which from 1874–80 sold 12,680 tons of copper for £56,000.

To some extent the decline in mineral traffic was masked by the freight from brickworks and granite quarries on Hingston Down and by the arsenic, some of which was exported to Antwerp. When the directors in 1882 reviewed ten years of working they found grounds for reasonable optimism. The original estimate of 50,000 tons a year had on the whole been maintained and even, on occasions, exceeded. If only passengers could be carried and the service linked to a main-line system, the future seemed bright. Certain events then taking place in the neighbourhood brought this ambition nearer fulfilment.

The London & South Western Railway had been flirting with the prospect of coming to North Cornwall, with the twin aims of getting an independent line to Plymouth and of capturing a passenger and freight trade to which the South Devon seemed indifferent. On 17 May 1876 it was running through Tavistock into Plymouth—albeit over the South Devon Railway's track.

Within a fortnight of this happening a four-horse coach service began running from Tavistock through Gunnislake and Callington to Liskeard. One of the sponsors of this enterprise, established by the East Cornwall & South Western Coach Company was, significantly, Edward Nicolls, who explained that the service was being promoted because Callington 'had hitherto been greatly neglected for want of railway accommodation and this would now be in a measure supplied'.

But the new enterprise, although served by a 'magnificent vehicle, all but new, built for a member of the Four-in-Hand Club, regardless of cost and . . . the very perfection of style and convenience'[10] was far from being a railway. It was in 1881 that there suddenly appeared, almost simultaneously, details of three separate railway schemes, each in its way designed to give Calstock, Gunnislake and Callington a passenger and goods link with a main line.

The first and most important of these plans, promoted by the Devon & Cornwall Central Railway (a body which originated in an earlier proposal to bring a line from Okehampton through Bodmin and Truro), was to bring a line from the junction shared at Lydford by the South Western and the South Devon Railways through the parishes of Brentor, Lamerton, Sydenham Damerel and Milton Abbot and to cross the Tamar above Newbridge, Gunnislake. It would then run down the western bank of the river to join the

mineral railway 950 yd east from the top of the incline station. A
further stretch of railway less than a mile long was planned from the
mineral railway terminus at Kelly Bray to a field 'abutting the
public road from Callington'. This would have given Callington a
station.*

The scheme commended itself to the mineral line's directors
because it offered a direct connection with their system. Moreover,
behind it stood the prestige of the South Western, which lent tacit
approval. Its main drawback was that it appeared to have been
deliberately planned to run through a barren countryside (shades of
Thomas Woollcombe!), prominent in which was the great upland
waste of Heathfield, a cold, sour plateau littered with stony debris
on which little grew and fewer people lived.

It had the enthusiastic support of Edward Nicolls, who spared no
effort to promote it. He stumped up and down the lonely countryside addressing meetings in tiny lamp-lit parish rooms, canvassing
remote farmsteads and patiently explaining the scheme in the parlours of country houses. It was, he insisted, the best one for the
neighbourhood and all should support it. It would connect the two
counties in a way they had never been connected before. To a
crowded meeting in Gunnislake in February 1882 Nicolls painted a
vivid picture of the plight of the district through lack of a railway
to get its produce to the big marketing centres. Brickworks were
'perishing' and the terra-cotta and granite industries unable to develop 'in this age of fierce competition'. This was a poor compliment
to the mineral line, but the point of Nicolls's plea was that goods put
into trucks on the proposed line could be in London within six
hours. At a meeting at Lamerton in the house of William Skewes,

---

* Of the two other schemes, one, 4½ miles long, would have branched from the
South Devon system south of its Tavistock station, tunnelled under Morwell Down
and crossed the Tamar by an 80 ft high single-arch bridge to a terminus at Hatches
Green. The other, the shape of a large U, was to start from a similar point and cross
the Tamar near Morwellham to end close to the Rising Sun Inn, Gunnislake. Plans
for all three schemes can be seen today in the Devon County Record Office.

a well-known mining engineer, who had brought along the Devon Friendship mine band to add pace and harmony to the proceedings, Nicolls prophesied that the new railway would open up the Milton Abbot area to become 'the great dairy district of England'.

Pouring ridicule on the other two proposals Nicolls and his Callington lobby won public approval for the Lydford–Gunnislake line. Their triumph was rewarded by an empty and cynical gesture. On 16 November 1882, an appalling day of storm, wind and rain (rivalling so many people said, the 'railway weather' of the Tavistock–Launceston branch line opening in 1865), the 'cutting of the first sod of the Devon & Cornwall Central Railway' took place at a point 'a mile outside Callington'[11]. Regardless of the weather the whole of Callington was *en fête*; banners were out, shop fronts decorated, trees planted along the route for the occasion. In the town's centre an 'imitation granite eliptic arch with battlements' was put up, surmounted by a large star illuminated free of charge by the Callington Gas Company. There were military bands, tableaux of the neighbourhood's industries and 500 children walked in procession in the bitter wind. 'Nothing of the kind had ever been seen in Callington before.'

But it was all an elaborate charade. Not the paper-borne Devon & Cornwall Railway but the South Western was the real power behind the scenes, and its agent indicated in speeches at the ceremony that the company was far too heavily engaged in promoting a bill for a separate line to Plymouth to think of putting Gunnislake and Callington on the railway map; the time would come but it was not now. And so the Sunday-school children went home, the tableaux were dismantled and the weather cleared up. A few cut turves remained to mark the only work ever done on the Devon & Cornwall Central Railway.

The East Cornwall Mineral line pursued an uncertain but still useful existence. Its goods trucks were carrying granite and bricks in increasing numbers but less arsenic and ore from the mines. A

M

special meeting of shareholders on 6 June 1882 had approved the sale of the undertaking to the Devon & Cornwall Central Railway Board, which had hinted at using it as a passenger line, and the ceremony at Callington seemed to confirm the wisdom of their choice. But now, suddenly, the South Western, unhappy since 1876 at having to run into Plymouth over South Devon metals, boldly pursued its own scheme for an independent approach to the port. From Lydford a subsidiary company, the Plymouth Devonport & South Western Junction, carried a new double-track line to Tavistock, and then swinging down the right bank of the Tavy to Bere Alston it accomplished the improbable geographical feat of entering Plymouth from London in a west–east direction. By its Act of Incorporation (25 August 1883) it was authorized to construct 28 miles of new railway from Devonport to Lydford and to make a junction with the East Cornwall Mineral Railway near Calstock. The dream of Edward Nicolls was coming true, but not quite in the way, nor as soon as, he had anticipated.

Waterloo was a long way from Calstock and the history of previous railway plans in the neighbourhood did not encourage optimism. The mineral line's annual meeting in 1886 heard a dispiriting story of trade depression and falling receipts. Arsenic production had almost ceased in most of the mines and the few concerns still working—Drakewalls, Gunnislake Clitters and Hingston Down—were in a poor way. Holmbush mine at Kelly Bray had been a good customer (1,748 tons of arsenic and 2,756 tons of copper were sold from the mine in 1886), but the company working it was heading for liquidation and hopes of a strong revival of local mining were dwindling. Almost half a century earlier the same complaints in almost identical language were being made by the disillusioned directors of the Tavistock Canal. But fate was kinder to the struggling mineral line. The South Western directors honoured their word. As the Plymouth Devonport & South Western Junction Railway (see Chapter Eleven), their eagerly awaited independent line to

Devonport was opened in June 1890 and the East Cornwall Mineral line finally taken over in June 1891.

The actual purchase was completed on 4 January 1894 but it continued as a mineral line under the ownership of the PD & SWJ until its conversion for passenger traffic in 1908. Payment was made by the issue of £48,250 ordinary shares, £21,500 in cash and a rent charge of £250 a year. Almost to the last the directors were complaining of poor trade, profits of only £394 being made in the second half of 1897, the last period for which accounts were published separately from those of the parent line. In 1908 it was said that its traffic had been averaging 70,000 tons a year, but this was probably an optimistic assessment. The carriage of mineral ore in its last years had practically ceased and by 1893 only three depots out of the original nine on the line were open[12]. Nevertheless for thirty-six years, without a major mishap, it had been the faithful servant of industry and agriculture in the area and the chief prop of Calstock as a river port. Much of the granite which London contractors so prized and which built Dover breakwater began the first part of its long journey from the quarries over the mineral line's steeply graded tracks. So too did much of the brick used in the building of the Morice Town section of Devonport dockyard. To farmers it brought lime and manures cheaply inland, and its coal trucks fed many of the industries of the neighbourhood.

When its incline ceased to work in 1908 and traffic instead went through to Bere Alston over the handsome new viaduct, Calstock withered and died as a port, and shipping vanished from the Tamar.

CHAPTER TEN

The Hingston Down Mines

As his car climbs the steep hill out of Gunnislake a visitor entering Cornwall for the first time comes suddenly upon a strange and tumbled landscape—a landscape of roofless and windowless mine engine houses, solitary chimneys and overgrown dumps set amid a bleak and almost treeless upland.

With only slight variations he will see this picture for the next 5 miles until he passes the bold chimney-crowned hump of Kit Hill, 1,000 ft above sea level. For Kit Hill, lying north of the one-time mining centre of Callington, marks the end of a highly mineralized tract of country where for over 500 years men have dug and burrowed for minerals. In the early and middle years of the nineteenth century particularly this bare and windswept granite ridge was ransacked for copper, tin, lead and silver in workings whose silent levels and narrow crooked shafts are now filled with water. Wherever men dug or excavated to any depth in the neighbourhood mineral ores were found. The quarry working adjoining Hingston Down mine uncovered a copper lode and at Drakewalls, when the embankment for the East Cornwall Mineral Railway was being excavated in 1870 a tin lode valued at £17 a fathom was found which the mining company promptly began working.

Unfold a 2½-in map of the area between Gunnislake and Callington and examine on it the ground either side of the main road linking the two towns. It is peppered with the map-maker's symbols for shafts and disused mine workings. Yet even so the map tells only part of the story. Over an area of country about 5 miles long and 4 miles wide within the parishes of Calstock, Callington and Stoke Climsland there are over eighty known mines, and probably an even greater number of unknown trials. For many there are no reliable records of output; but when even the incomplete figures are added up some remarkable statistics emerge. Taking only those mines where the yield of copper ore has exceeded 300 tons, a total of 240,771 tons of copper ore was brought to the surface between 1815 and 1909, yielding 13,145 tons of fine copper. Almost two-thirds of this amount was produced between 1850 and 1880. The output of black tin from three mines in the area between 1852 and 1909 was over 25,000 tons, while silver-lead mines in the three parishes produced over 33,000 oz of silver and nearly 9,000 tons of lead ore.*

All but a bare handful of the mines concerned stopped long before the end of the last century. Few of them exceeded 100 fathoms in depth and many were as shallow as 60 fathoms and employed less than fifty hands. Until the building of the East Cornwall Mineral Railway in 1872 all of them sent their ores by horse and cart to Calstock for weighing, sampling and despatch down the Tamar.

Many of these mines exist today only as small depressions or mounds in fields, while for others the only clue is a trickle of ochre-coloured water from a half-hidden adit.

DRAKEWALLS MINE

The oldest and richest of these workings was Drakewalls, the mine whose strange ruins greet the visitor at the top of Gunnislake Hill and which stopped working in 1910. The position of the mineral deposits is marked by a great excavation and a long run of broken ground. Subordinate branches of the main tin lode occur as veins or stringers near the surface and these have been worked from ancient

---

* The production figures are those of the Geological Survey. Figures of the value of ores mined are based on the estimates of J. H. Collins, a West Country mining expert.

times as a stockwork, a method akin to open-cast mining. The huge
excavations or gunnises are over 60 ft deep. The engine shaft is sunk
to 190 fathoms on the main tin lode, which with its branches is said
to have yielded £350,000 worth of minerals, including some arsenic.
To the north, several copper lodes were worked. Drakewalls's riches
have earned it the title of 'the Dolcoath of East Cornwall'; between
1875 and 1883 the company working it obtained £218,000-worth of
tin around the 80-fathom level without having to sink as much as
6 ft of shaft.

Drakewalls became the first mine in the country to use a process
which separated tin from wolfram, the resulting tungstate of soda
being sold for £14 a ton to the Manchester textile industry.* Because of the mine's long life the surface buildings are in different
states of decay. Below, so much ground has been taken away that
great underground caverns exist which can be traversed only by
boat. The full extent of these was not appreciated until the 1880s,
when the deep adit being driven northwards under the open-cast
workings broke into an area 'of huge chasms hundreds of fathoms
in length where the rock has been taken away in previous mining
operations'. This adit drains into the Tamar about 600 yd west of
Weir Head and the mine can be entered from it where it emerges
from the hillside at Hatches Green.

The site today is divided by the road from Gunnislake to Calstock. The northern half of the mine saw most of the copper production. In the southern half the tin working is readily distinguished
by the reddish colouring of the rock. At the bottom of the engine
shaft near here tin is reputed to have glistened 'like a diamond
shop'. Ruins of the arsenic-burning furnaces are nearby. The derelict building with the ivy-clad stack at the top of the hill housed the
crushing stamps. Below it are the remains of a pumping-engine

---

* This was in 1845–56, and was known as the Oxland process, after its inventor.
Oxland put up the machinery at his own expense and supplied the necessary soda
free.

house and a whim or hauling-engine house, the latter belonging to the 1870s period of working. The curiously foreshortened appearance of some of the chimneys is due to the top course of bricks having been removed.

Gunnislake Old (copper, tin and uranium)

Gunnislake grew up around this mine, and its ivy-mantled stack and engine house (threatened with demolition) dating from 1864 mark Michael's shaft. Opened towards the end of the eighteenth century it is reputed to have produced over £250,000 worth of ore in the 1820s. It included East Gunnislake mine and was worked in conjunction with Wheal Tamar (later South Bedford mine) on the Tamar's Devon bank. The so-called East Liscombe lode, developed in the latter mine, ran under the river into the East Gunnislake workings where a shaft on the Cornish bank was pumped by flat rods carried across the Tamar on a trestle bridge above Weir Head from a water-wheel at Wheal Tamar—a unique example of a Devon mine pumping a Cornish one. Old plans reveal heavy stoping under the river bed around the lode. Uranium (torbernite) was found in Old Gunnislake mine about 90 fathoms from surface; then of little value it was used for colouring glass. Its greenish appearance led to two of the lodes being named Great Green and Little Green lode. The mine was abandoned about 1883.

Gunnislake Clitters (arsenic, copper, tin, umber and wolfram)

This mine is almost wholly in granite and its engine shaft, 276 fathoms below adit, is one of the deepest in the area. Beginning as an adit trial from the Tamar it produced tin and copper in 1822–7. Starting up again in the 1860s it had in 1865 a new 40-in cylinder engine with a 10-ft stroke built in the Bedford Foundry, Tavistock. The engine's boiler weighed 11 tons and developed 50 psi. A 30-hp whim engine drew ores from the 90-fathom level. From then until

1900 it produced, according to the Geological Survey, 33,310 tons of 8¼ per cent copper ore and 10 tons of black tin.

After 1900 it was amalgamated with Hingston Down Consols and the adjoining Hawkmoor and Gunnislake Old mine. The new company introduced a milling method for ore then new to this country, profitably retrieving a huge dump of burnt leavings from previous workings. From 1902–09 the mine treated nearly 450 tons of wolfram. In the 1920s it was linked with Hingston Down mine by a mono-cable railway, some of the masonry support pillars still existing. Gunnislake Clitters was one of the few mines to remain a substantial producer into the twentieth century, selling—according to Collins—nearly £83,000 worth of black tin, wolfram, arsenic and copper between 1902 and 1909.

Gunnislake Clitters was abandoned in the late 1920s, although there has recently been renewed interest in treating its dumps. These and the ruins of two engine houses, a treatment mill and some flues remain a conspicuous feature of the landscape between Chilsworthy and Gunnislake. Much of the arsenic produced on the mine was treated in the adjoining Greenhill arsenic works, whose tall chimney halfway up the hillside dominates the country for miles around. These works originally consisted of a large precipitating and arsenic-refining plant built in 1875 to treat ores from Holmbush, Kelly Bray and Wheal Newton. Lack of capital caused them to close down shortly afterwards but they were restarted in 1901. Arsenical mundic was then brought from Wheal Crebor and other mines, treated, packed into casks made on the premises and shipped from Calstock quays until the 1930s.

Hingston Down Consols (arsenic, copper, fluorspar, iron, tin and wolfram)

Lying to the west of Gunnislake Clitters, this was started in 1843 and last actively worked in 1926. Two lodes run through it about 30 ft apart. While working for tin in 1858 a large copper lode was discovered 100 ft from the surface, the mine being looked upon as one of the best in the two counties. In another part of the workings at the same time miners 600 ft down discovered a live frog, which caused almost as much sensation as the discovery of the copper lode[1]. Between 1850 and 1880 Hingston Down produced 64,000 tons of copper as well as arsenical pyrites and some black tin, but in the years immediately before the first world war wolfram was the main product. In 1906 fluorspar was encountered in a deposit 20 ft wide and 25 ft thick. A ruined engine house still standing, put up in the 1880s, is unusual in having a flat roof with a parapet round it; most mine engine houses in the neighbourhood had a hipped roof. Malachite, copper pyrites and fluorspar can be picked up on its dumps.

Prince of Wales (arsenic, copper, iron, lead, silver and tin)

Lies south-west of Hingston Down mine. The reddish hue of its extensive dumps by the road from Harrowbarrow to St Ann's Chapel betray the tin found in a mine first worked for copper. Except for short interruptions, this mine worked from 1863 until 1914, and besides 10,845 tons of copper ore it produced over 1,000 tons of more valuable black tin, as well as 7,720 tons of iron pyrites which yielded arsenic. The amounts of silver and lead recovered were comparatively small. The main ore body in this mine, known as the Prince of Wales's lode, has been 'lost' through being cut off by a 'slide' of ground, and the prospect of rediscovering it makes Prince of Wales an attractive proposition if mineral working is resumed in the area. In the last war a milling plant put up adjoining the engine house marking the site of Watson's shaft, treated ore from the dumps and reopened adits of a number of mines in the neighbourhood, notably the small Ding Dong working near Tavistock.

Wheal Brothers (arsenic, silver-lead, copper, iron, tin and lead)

This is south of the main road from Gunnislake to Callington, in an area known as Silver Valley from its quantity of small mines which produced silver or silver lead, among them Wheal Langford, Wheal Fortune and Wheal St Vincent. Wheal Brothers started as Wheal Duchy about 1812, then being a copper prospect. Silver was found in a 'leader' 1–4 in wide which yielded over £5,000 worth of ore, sufficient to pay the initial expenses. After this it was abandoned, to be restarted in 1833 as Wheal Brothers, when its silver was sold at prices varying from £2 to £500 a ton. In three months in 1833 nearly £6,000 worth was sold, and in the following four months dividends of nearly £9,000 were paid. This led to the opening of neighbouring *Wheal Sisters* on the eastern part of the lode in 1863, while the so-called *Silver Valley* mine to the west was also worked in conjunction with it. All these mines ceased production before the end of the last century, although some exploratory work was done for wolfram in the Silver Valley mine in 1943. The buildings of Wheal Langford are now incorporated in a farm.

Wheal Arthur and *Wheal Edward* (arsenic, copper, blende, iron, lead, tin and wolfram)

These make up part of the remarkable mining scenery between Gunnislake and Calstock, and lie between the Tamar and the railway from Calstock to Gunnislake. Wheal Arthur, closer to the Tamar, began working in 1850 and was active at intervals until 1926. Wheal Edward, due west of it, was started in 1836 but closed down, to restart in 1850 working the same lode as Wheal Arthur; the mines are interconnected. Wheal Arthur was the larger, paying out dividends of over £7,000 in 1840–54.

Calstock Consols (copper and silver lead)

Its ruins are prominent beside the disused cutting of the old East Cornwall Mineral Railway above Calstock; it included the setts of neighbouring Wheal Zion and the Danescombe Valley mine. It was at work in 1822, but its busiest period seems to have been between

1847 and 1858, when over 3,000 tons of copper ore was raised. The surface buildings to be seen today date from this time. Some stamps erected here in 1851, when the mine employed over eighty people, were named the 'Bentinck stamps' in honour of 'the great advocate of human industry Lord George Bentinck'[2]. There was an ambitious plan in 1909 to work the Danescombe sett of this mine for arsenic, which was to be treated at the Rumleigh arsenic works on the Devon side of the river; but this fell into abeyance. Although never a large producer, this mine's ruins have a picturesque importance today.

Okel Tor (arsenic, copper, iron, tin and lead)

This in its heyday was one of the most important mines near Calstock, and its busy, extensive workings on the river bank opposite Gawton mine used to fascinate paddle-steamer passengers in the 1870s. The Great Cross Course which shifted the main lode at Devon Great Consols also dislocates the main lode here. The mine was restarted in 1850 mainly to work a lead lode which was then more in evidence than copper, although it went on to produce only 2 tons of lead. In 1850–51 the company working it built a quay capable of taking vessels of up to 200 tons, thus saving the cost of horse-hauling the ore to Calstock[3]. The main engine shaft, which still has part of its engine house intact, reaches 80 fathoms below the level of the Tamar, and the main copper lode passes under the river into Gawton mine.

Although it produced 213 tons of black tin, the mine mainly raised copper (13,215 tons) and arsenic in its later years. In 1883 it worked with Cotehele Consols in the Danescombe Valley, treating the iron pyrites from that mine for arsenic. There are still extensive ruins of the arsenic-treatment plant, including part of the line of flues which terminated in the stack whose stump (shorn of its top course of bricks) stands near the railway. Okel Tor stopped active working in 1887.

New Great Consols (arsenic, blende, copper, gold, iron, silver, tin and wolfram)

Its workings, representing nearly 100 years of mining activity, dominate the village of Luckett. When reopening plans were announced in 1947, they brought hopes of a real revival of mining in the Tamar Valley. It has been worked under various names, including Wheal Martha, since before 1830, when some tin was obtained; but the ores, although varied, are scattered, fragmentary and complex and exceedingly difficult to treat. Extensive arsenic works were erected in the 1870s when 250 people were employed, and later a combined mechanical and chemical treatment process was employed which could recover copper and arsenic as well as gold and silver.

When the mine reopened in 1947 it had not been seriously worked underground since 1881. By driving in an easterly direction towards the granite from the old engine shaft on the north side of the valley, it was hoped to reach tin. Some crushing mills were put up about a quarter of a mile away, connected with the shaft by an aerial ropeway. Two electric pumps drained water into a reservoir at the 40-fathom level, and from there it was pumped to the adit. The company was, however, continually delayed by pump breakdowns, and an incessant battle with water. Much of the water in the deeper levels was so corrosive that it formed an instant film of copper whenever it touched exposed ironwork, and air and water pipes had frequently to be renewed. On the other hand timber, often over seventy years old, was found to be thoroughly preserved by the copper. Hot springs were frequently encountered. One spring at the 96-fathom level, where the lode was being driven on, bubbled from the floor at 80 degrees F, giving off gas bubbles and containing sodium sulphate.

By 1951 the mill on the mine was recovering about 10 lb of black tin to a ton, but the complexity of the ores and the cost of working doomed the venture to failure. It was abandoned in 1954, having produced 170 tons of black tin and 2 tons of wolfram. The cost of reopening—£400,000 of largely American capital of which only £100,000 was recovered—illustrates the hazards of metalliferous mining in Cornwall[4].

Holmbush and *Redmoor* (arsenic, copper, fluorspar, iron, lead, silver, tin and wolfram)

With Kelly Bray mine, these formed a group later known as Callington United Mines, working a richly mineralized triangle of country containing copper, tin and arsenic as well as an important silver-lead lode. The dumps of Holmbush mine, together with the remains of some engine houses, can be seen by the side of the Stoke Climsland road. Holmbush was working early in the eighteenth century and continued with intervals of suspension until 1923. From the great north–south trending lead lode over £135,000 worth of ore has been extracted, and from 1822–64 some 36,000 tons of copper ore were sold for about £280,000. Towards the end of the century arsenic, fluorspar and a certain amount of wolfram were mined, and some work was carried out on the dumps in the early 1920s. The settlement of Kelly Bray grew up around this mine, which with neighbouring workings was the principal employer in the district; in the 1840s it had over 250 men. Redmoor mine, which is connected with Holmbush at the 90-fathoms level, spreads on either side of a road running south-west from Kelly Bray, and has produced copper, silver, lead and tin. The southern end of the Holmbush lead lode comes into Redmoor, and between 1843 and 1883 lead ore to the value of £120,000 was sold. In 1844 the mine had a notorious hauling engine with a horizontal locomotive-type boiler which had 'the singular appearance of a locomotive stuck in the mud'. It was named 'Grout's puffer' (after Joseph Grout, the chairman of the company) and the *Mining Journal* noted that 'it will prove at least advantageous to the neighbouring meadows, as the condensation of immense columns of steam issuing therefrom will answer the purpose of irrigation'. Some prospecting was done at Redmoor in 1943.

Kit Hill (arsenic, blende, copper, fluorspar, tin and wolfram)

These mines on the slopes of Kit Hill were, along with Drakewalls and the Prince of Wales's mine, the principal tin producers in the area, although their total output was never large. On Kit Hill itself tin debris can be found, and prospecting on it and under it has been carried on for hundreds of years. Kit Hill Great Consols is in the granite at the summit of the hill, and the principal workings are near the chimney at the top—which together with the now-demolished engine house was built (although not on the site it now occupies) in 1856. The lodes near the chimney yielded tin ore and wolfram in association with copper, mispickel and blende, but in small amounts. Below this mine was South Kithill, while to the right of it was East Kithill, with a dump by the side of the road to Kelly Bray.

Two tunnels, or strictly speaking adits, were driven underneath Kit Hill. The longest, the Excelsior tunnel, was driven from the Deer Park plantation on the north of Kit Hill south-by-west towards the north engine shaft of Kit Hill Consols. This was begun in 1877 and restarted in 1881, being driven straight for 350 fathoms; but after the discovery of only one good bunch of ore it was abandoned before reaching the engine shaft. The tunnel was prolonged for a further 50 yd in 1938, and then driven a short distance south-east to test the ground for tin and wolfram, the work being done by drills fed from an air compressor at the adit mouth. A series of experiments for underground atomic explosion tests took place in the tunnel in 1959. On the south side of Kit Hill is a similar tunnel, driven for about half a mile with the intention originally of connecting with the Deer Park tunnel.

It is difficult to separate quarry from mine workings on Kit Hill today, so thoroughly has the whole area been excavated, dug, tunnelled and mined for stone and minerals. The stack of the old Kit Hill mine which crowns its height has been preserved for a landmark by the Duchy of Cornwall.

CHAPTER ELEVEN

The Coming of the South Western

THE $22\frac{1}{2}$ miles of double track laid between 1887 and 1890 to give the London & South Western Railway a line under its control from Plymouth through the Tamar Valley to Waterloo was almost the last major piece of railway construction undertaken in Devon and Cornwall by a main-line company.

Its completion brought in, almost overnight, an electrifying atmosphere of change which led to some of the fiercest and liveliest railway competition that had yet been seen in Devon and Cornwall. The South Western gained the lion's share of an important and valuable fruit and flower traffic which the Great Western was still struggling to regain when war broke out in 1914. At the same time it spelled the doom of the Tamar. From this time on the river began to decline as an important waterway, for the trains drew passengers away from the steamers and cargoes from the barges. Many of the little ferries which had crossed for centuries from bank to bank gradually ceased to ply their trade. This process was completed when the new line was linked to the narrow-gauge East Cornwall Mineral Railway.

The early steps which led the South Western to the perimeter of the Tamar Valley have been related in Chapter Nine. The running of its standard-gauge trains to Plymouth (which began in 1876) over the South Devon Railway's mixed-gauge track from Lydford was not a comfortable arrangement; as trade grew, relationships and working became more and more uneasy and clumsy; equally onerous was the South Devon's demand for a rent of $10\frac{1}{2}$ pennies in every shilling of the South Western's gross receipts.

The answer to these difficulties—a separate line to Plymouth—

Adit on the Marquis lode at Bedford United mine above Gunnislake. Some of the original timbering can be seen

Excelsior Tunnel near Luckett. Begun in 1881 and continued at intervals until 1938, the tunnel runs nearly 400 fathoms into Kit Hill and was dug with the object (never completed) of connecting to the bottom of Kit Hill mine

Water-wheel (now demolished) typical of many once used in the Tamar Valley area. The method of bringing water by overhead launder is well illustrated. This wheel was at Hexworthy, on Dartmoor

was provided by a subsidiary, the Plymouth Devonport & South Western Junction Railway, which in August 1883 secured powers to connect Plymouth with the South Western's system at Lydford, with the stipulation that the East Cornwall Mineral Railway should be linked with the new line by a branch from Bere Alston. Although the South Western undertook to work the line, the Plymouth company, which now also owned the East Cornwall Mineral Railway, was fully constituted in its own right, with a capital eventually totalling almost £1,000,000. It had an impressive board of directors, including the Earl of Mount Edgcumbe, Lord St Levan and the Duke of Bedford, who between them parted with nearly all the land needed for the projected railway for £25,000 in fully paid-up shares.

BUILDING THE LINE

The total cost was £793,000. Work began on 2 March 1887, engaging for nearly three years the combined efforts of nearly 2,000 men who, during the building, had to shift 2,500,000 tons of earth, 'a larger quantity than was ever dealt with in railway works in the West of England over a similar period'. It was still the era of railway navvies, but never were they to be seen in such numbers again in Devon and Cornwall. As the line neared Plymouth the contractors, W. T. Relf and J. Pethick, bought in Devonport dockyard 'for the price of old iron' the naval hulk HMS *Bittern*. Her decks cut down, she was fitted with bunks for 120 men and moored in the Tavy to become the floating home for two years of the men who built the Tavy viaduct and adjoining stretches of line. From the start the navvies' personal welfare was the close concern of the Earl of Mount Edgcumbe. He had a mission hall built at Bere Alston, staffed with a missioner, and to curb the temptation to strong drink he supplied free coffee. Whether or not it was the coffee, less than a dozen cases of drunkenness among the navvies were reported during the whole

N

period; and 'I do not know of any railway where the men have been
treated with so much kindliness by the inhabitants,' declared one of
the contractors at a dinner in Tavistock market for over 800 of the
navvies in January 1888[1].

They worked hard for their living. The section from Lydford to
Tavistock presented no special difficulties[2], but from then onwards
as the line crept along the high ridge of ground between the Tamar
and Tavy Valleys it abounded in cuttings and embankments calling
for deep excavations. At Shilla Mill south-west of Tavistock the
track ran into the hard shoulder of Morwell Down, whose toughness
seventy years earlier had held up the construction of the Tavistock
Canal. Through this rock a 600-yd tunnel was bored on an 'S'
curve, disturbing a copper lode in the process. From the tunnel it
was high ground all the way to Bere Alston, whose station stands as
high as Calstock church on the 400-ft contour level[3].

To keep the maximum gradient as easy as possible—the steepest
section of the line is 1 in 72—massive earth moving was necessary
between Bere Alston and Bere Ferrers. At Lockeridge just outside
Bere Alston an embankment nearly 230 yd long absorbed almost
140,000,000 cubic yd of rock. Less than a mile farther on at Bere
Ferrers came the deepest cutting on the line (63 ft), with its adjoining embankment nearly as high.

Near here the Tavy broadens to join the Tamar and over two
years were occupied in building the £50,000 viaduct across it. The
eight bow-string girders, each of 112-ft span, rest on masonry approaches at each end and, to secure firm foundations in the bed of
the Tavy, iron cylinders 8 ft diameter of $1\frac{3}{4}$-in iron were sunk in
sections into the river bed, where 'heavy weights were placed on
them so that they gradually cut their way into the rock'. Rock was
reached at 80 ft and the cylinders were filled with concrete. Such
methods, it was claimed, had they been known thirty years earlier,
would have simplified Brunel's task of bridging the Tamar. The
$\frac{1}{2}$-mile embankment by the Tamar, along which the train travels

before it swings inland for Devonport and Plymouth, was constructed on land reclaimed a hundred years earlier. Known as the
'Tamerton Flat', it is the fastest and straightest portion of the line
between Plymouth and Tavistock and has been covered in twenty-
four seconds.

After Devonport and Friary (Plymouth) stations, Tavistock was
the most important station on the line and efforts were made to give
it buildings to match. Laid out over a 5-acre site with a down
platform 350 ft long, it incorporated interesting examples of late
Victorian station decoration. The upper windows in the main buildings had variously tinted cathedral glass, while mirrors and fire-
places in the waiting rooms and former buffet bar were in iron
frames designed to imitate wood. The 'snail creep' masonry (i.e.
stones laid 'on end') of the main buildings was distinctive and was
repeated on Brentor station.[4]

The completed line had seventy-six bridges, of which seven were
viaducts, and despite the curves and embankments withstood without a tremor the thrust of the 6 ft 7 in coupled driving wheels of the
tall chimney Adams' express engines which hauled the South
Western's principal passenger trains at the period when the line was
opened. For working it, the South Western took 50 per cent of the
gross profits with a maximum rebate of £15,650 a year on all
through traffic.[5]

With the authority of its own line behind it, the South Western
speeded up the 229-mile journey from Waterloo to Plymouth by
30 to 40 minutes, almost all the time being made up between
Exeter and Plymouth.* The best Great Western trains to Exeter and

---

* They seldom ran to time, however. The best train of the day was supposed to
take 5 hours 10 minutes, but the down expresses were frequently 15 to 20 minutes
late reaching Tavistock, delaying local trains. The Okehampton train in consequence
was often 3 hours late reaching Plymouth. The evening train from Bere Alston to
Plymouth was not infrequently 1½ hours late in leaving and even then lost 10
minutes on the 10-mile journey to Plymouth. The South Western's bad time-
keeping was a frequent source of comment in the press of the day. See WDM
22–29 August 1899.

Plymouth were quicker, but they did not carry third-class passengers. The South Western did so without any surcharge and by
1896 it was building an advanced style of tri-composite coach for
its Plymouth route with lavatory access for all three classes. The
most famous trains using the main line were the Ocean Liner trains
in 1903–4.

TRAFFIC AND DIVIDENDS

Local traffic justified earlier hopes and forecasts. On the day the
line opened (2 June 1890) 1,000 booked to travel from Plymouth to
Tavistock, the first train leaving Plymouth at 6.53 a.m. Bere Alston
became so popular as an excursion centre that the elderly landlady
of the Edgcumbe Arms, the only inn in the village, was run off her
feet. The morning the line opened thirty people presented themselves for breakfast, an invasion quite beyond her resources. It took
her a week to reorganize things and by then the Edgcumbe Arms
had become the Edgcumbe Hotel, a title it has borne ever since.

An unexpected but lucrative traffic, which lasted until the outbreak of war, were the school treats. Typical was an afternoon in
June 1901, when 850 children and 550 adults poured out from
Sunday schools in Plymouth, Stonehouse and Devonport into
special trains to picnic spots around Bere Alston. The new railway
also enforced a widely welcome revision of postal arrangements over
a large part of Devon and Cornwall. A fast newspaper train left
Devonport at 3.50 a.m., reaching Barnstaple and other North Devon
towns in time for letters and newspapers to be included in the
second morning delivery[6].

But the fruit growers benefited most. The Great Western's lazily
held distribution monopoly toppled almost overnight. Within a
month nearly all the fruit traffic previously using Saltash station had
been diverted to Bere Alston, from where three trains daily took it

to Waterloo in the season. This traffic was gained mainly by better timing and competitive selling. The South Western wooed its customers with persistence and skill. Astonished market gardeners and farmers found the company's agents coming into their fields and buying their produce on the spot while porters stood behind ready to pack it. The heavily laden and scented strawberry wagons which had previously plodded to Saltash were now diverted to Cotehele quay, the packed fruit being ferried over the river for 1d a box to be met by the railway's vans on the Devon side. From here it went to Bere Alston station over the Earl of Mount Edgcumbe's private drive, his lordship turning a benevolent eye on traffic which bolstered his dividends. So rich were the pickings from this early strawberry traffic that the London & North Western began to send its own vans to Cotehele by agreement with the South Western. Some loaded road vans were transferred straight to rail trucks at Bere Alston for Waterloo, and thence driven to Euston.

The Great Western's response was to adopt similar tactics in the Cargreen and St Mellion areas, for which Saltash was the most convenient station. This was truly Great Western territory but even here it brushed shoulders with the bustling South Western agents, who had produce ferried across the river from Cargreen to Bere Ferrers station where wagons were waiting. Such enterprise put new life into the fruit growers. Large new areas came under strawberry cultivation in Stoke Climsland and even, of all unlikely places, on the lower slopes of Cadson Bury, a prehistoric earthwork near Callington, from where in 1890 strawberries were sent to the wholesale markets in London, Glasgow and Edinburgh. Plum orchards were extensively planted around Bere Alston and a jam factory opened at Weir Quay. Rents and land prices rose, and when in 1898 a fruit growers' co-operative was established with a depot at Weir Quay its 5s shares were over-subscribed by the public.

Between 1896 and 1907 the amount of general freight handled in and out of Tavistock station doubled to reach 17,000 tons a year.

Much of this was coal which a few years earlier had come up the
river to Morwellham and thence by canal to Tavistock, but there
were more unusual loads. Four-ton trucks took away rinded oak
bark from the Bedford and Mount Edgcumbe estates. This was
used for tanning; the hands, clothes and faces of the men handling
it would be stained red with the rind sap. A load of 50 tons of jam
went to Woolwich in 1899 and 562 cases to Middlesborough. This,
for troops in the Boer War, was sent from the factory at Weir Quay,
which a few years earlier had been smelting silver. Granite came
from the Merrivale quarries near Tavistock, while wolfram, yellow
ochre (for paint) mundic, ore, arsenic, tin and copper precipitate
frequently appear in the despatch record books[8].

The PD & SWJ, its line worked for it at 'less than cost price', sat
back to draw dividends. These were a moderate 2 per cent in the
first years, although in 1896 they might well have been higher but
for an inexplicable and unsuccessful application to the Railway
Commissioners to introduce through fares from Cornish stations on
the Great Western to stations on the South Western system via the
newly opened railway. The application cost the company £1,103,
which the *Railway Magazine* reckoned knocked almost $\frac{1}{2}$ per cent
off the dividend[9]. By the end of December 1906, however, dividends
of $4\frac{3}{4}$ per cent were being paid on the ordinary shares.

THE LINK WITH CORNWALL

The new line, however, principally benefited only one side of the
valley; a direct rail link to London was still denied the industries
and inhabitants of Calstock, Gunnislake and Callington, although
they had been pressing for it since 1863. The traveller from Waterloo or Exeter to Calstock still faced the cumbersome business of
alighting with his baggage at Tavistock and catching a four-horse
coach to complete his journey. From Plymouth the best approach to

Calstock was by steamer. The tardiness of the PD & SWJ directors in connecting the west banks of the Tamar with their new line to Tavistock did not go unnoticed.

The Great Western, smarting under its rival's tactics, had been considering having a nominee company build a light railway from Saltash to Callington which would effectively tap the granite and fruit traffic of the Calstock, St Dominic and St Mellion areas. This revival of an old idea was much to the liking of market gardeners in the St Mellion area, now the principal strawberry growers in the Valley, for they paid heavy horse-haulage costs. In July 1899 a scheme was submitted by the Callington Light Railway Development Company with the benevolent encouragement of the Great Western. Although almost immediately it became a casualty of the South African war,* it indirectly accomplished its object by forcing the PD & SWJ directors to submit a proposal of their own under the Light Railway Act of 1896. This was for a 3 ft 6 in gauge line, 4½ miles long, starting from Bere Alston and linking with the East Cornwall Mineral Railway just above Calstock. Almost half its estimated cost (£70,014 or £17,415 a mile) was for bridging the Tamar at Calstock.

The only solid objection to the proposal came from the sponsors of the proposed Saltash–Callington Railway, which not needing any expensive viaduct could be built for £10,000 a mile—at least £7,000 cheaper than the 'reckless and extravagant' Plymouth company's lines.† The evidence of a deputation from Callington in favour of the PD & SWJ's line weighed heavily with the Commissioners who pronounced that 'the junction of the two lines was a reasonable thing to make', permission being confirmed on 13 July 1900.

But capital became difficult to obtain as interest in railway matters

* This scheme was not in fact officially abandoned until 1924. In 1865 an Act had been secured by a Saltash & Callington Railway Company for a line between these two places but no work was ever done.

† The Great Western also opposed it but was ruled out as having no *locus standi* in the matter.

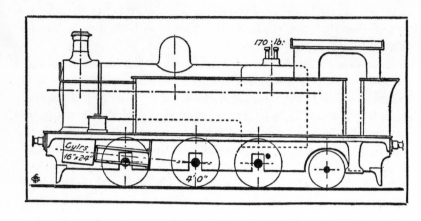

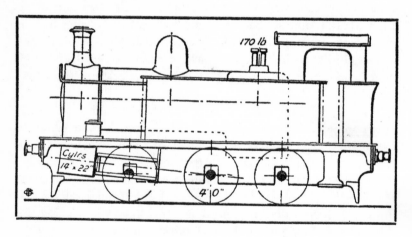

PD & SW 0–6–2T passenger locomotive and 0–6–0T goods locomotive
introduced in 1908

yielded to the Boer war. In 1903 the company had to obtain a second order extending until July 1906 its original completion time of five years. Before this was up a third order, obtained in 1905, had altered the gauge to 4 ft 8½ in and allowed the purchase of additional land. A fourth order in 1906 fixed the date of completion for 13 January 1908. Some of these delays were to have a sequel in the arbitration court.

Among the tenders submitted in 1904 for the new line was one for £48,995 from John Charles Lang, a public-works contractor of Liskeard. This was extraordinarily low and the engineers found many of Lang's calculations hopelessly wrong; he had so underestimated his quantities for building the viaduct that he was invited before the board to explain them. Lang in fact arrived in London with an amended tender of £54,680, of which £31,979 was his estimate for the bridge; this was still far below the original estimate but was accepted[10].

Few railway contracts go according to plan but that for the Bere Alston branch line proved a vintage one for difficulties. Acrimony arose from the conflicting personalities of the contractor and the engineers. The latter, W. R. Galbraith and Richard Church, had twenty years earlier supervised the construction of the Lydford–Plymouth line; but they were now older men with physical infirmities. Galbraith who 'was not strong and cannot bear much strain' never visited the works, exercising supervision from his London office. Richard Church, 'so deaf that he could only be spoken to through a tube', relied heavily on an overworked assistant. Lang's own supervising engineer, Harris, kept no daily diary but wrote one up from random notes which he then threw away. Lang found himself with a contract which stretched his resources to their limits, but held strong and obstinate opinions, in the absence of the engineers frequently making decisions over their heads. Finally there was Holman Fred Stephens, 'the light railway king', who buzzed up and down the line like a probing gadfly, annoying Lang and puzzling others until it transpired that he had been instructed by Church to supervise the reconversion of the track to standard gauge.

The $1\frac{3}{4}$-mile stretch from Bere Alston to the Tamar was completed more or less on time, but the $2\frac{1}{4}$-mile link on the Cornish side proved more formidable and was also slowed down drastically by trouble with landowners, for 'in accordance with the usual experience of railway companies people who had been clamorous for the building of the line asked exorbitant prices for the land and the company had to go to the Board of Trade for power to enter'. The Harewood cutting between Calstock and Gunnislake involved moving 41,000 cubic yd of earth and rock in skips running on a narrow-gauge tramway, the trolleys being hauled up a 1-in-4 gradient by horses. This work alone took two years and two months, Lang being repeatedly pressed by Church to use an engine to speed up haulage. Eventually he obtained the locomotive *Ada* from the old Devon Great Consols railway and horse-hauled it up Gunnislake hill to the site. But the engine was not powerful enough, and eventually a 'six-wheel locomotive' was obtained from W. T. Relf, the South Western Railway contractor. After this the rate of haulage rapidly improved. Altogether this cutting and other works between Calstock and Gunnislake involved the removal of 66,000 cubic yd of material and took over three years to complete.

But the viaduct was the biggest problem. It was the key to the railway; without it being completed on time neither half of the new line could be used. Miscalculations began at the start. Trial borings were made in May 1904 on each side of the river bank but none in the river bed. This proved a mistake, for while on the Devon side bedrock was at a comparatively shallow level, farther in the river towards the Cornish side it was necessary to go down 120 ft to find rock for the foundation of the ninth pillar. Unexpected beds of gravel obstructed the driving of piles for the coffer dams in the shelving river bed, and the pumps were frequently inadequate to keep out the water. A cable railway was rigged from bank to bank to transport some supplies, but almost all the sand and cement and much of the granite used was river-borne and was not always punctual in arriving. Altogether it took the whole of nine months to complete the ninth pier and almost two and a quarter years to finish the foundations of the bridge. This was much longer than the engineers had foreseen and Church, first through his assistant and later through a stream of personal notes, prodded Lang to employ more plant and men.

The real answer was continuous working round the clock, but Lang repeatedly ignored requests to put on a night shift, pleading labour difficulties. Church replied by open accusations of 'dilatory work', and complained in exasperation that 'in spite of constant requests that you will get on faster you seem to go slower and slower'. One of the dates set for the line's completion (30 April 1906) came and went, taking with it the company's hope of handling the 1906 fruit traffic. The Great Western, not a disinterested spectator of the delays in building the line, had instituted on 1 June 1904 a bus service between Albaston, Callington and Saltash, which was providing a popular and convenient link with its own trains. In 1906 Church's complaints to Lang came to a head following a mishap with the bridge abutment on the Devon side: the earth bank against which it rested had not been properly 'punned' causing it to shift and move the abutment $8\frac{1}{2}$ in out of plumb. Putting this right caused more delay and cost another £589.

But Lang also had grievances. He accused the engineers of leaving him for days without instructions, of long delays in providing him with plans, particularly for the bridges, while land was often not ready when he wanted to work it. The change of specification midway through the work meant the scrapping of the original Vignoles type of 60-lb rails and their substitution by standard-gauge weight, 82 lb a yard. These 'being a second hand lot did not go into place without a good deal of extra handling'. Lang finally put night gangs to work on the viaduct late in 1906 by which time Church was clearly threatening that the company would exact a penalty for delays.

On 11 May 1907 the last arch was finished and when a few months later the viaduct (which absorbed 11,148 cement blocks) was completed it had taken three years and seven months to build, twenty-seven months longer than the contract time allowed for the whole railway. The completed line from Bere Alston to its terminus at Kelly Bray was finally opened to the public on 2 March 1908.

The last act was played out in the arbitration court. Lang put in a claim for £29,508 for damages, expenses and extra work incurred in delays in waiting for plans. If accepted, this would have represented a cost of £20,000 a mile for building a light railway. The company in turn invoked its delay clause, claiming £10 a day for 410 days. After a nine days' hearing in London, a settlement was agreed conceding Lang £15,000—an acknowledgement that some of his complaints were not unjustified. In accepting this he had no reason to be ashamed of his finished work. His viaduct with its twelve arches each of 60-ft span and standing $117\frac{1}{2}$ ft above high water remains a far more graceful structure than Brunel's (although without the latter's engineering appeal), and lends a beauty of its own to the river scene at Calstock. With its completion East Cornwall had a direct railway link to London—something it had been waiting for since 1863.

The new line, however, still stopped a mile short of the name town of its title. To complete the journey to or from Kelly Bray, Callington people had to resort to a bus. In vain Venning pleaded with the board to extend the line to Callington; even a personal visit to London met a blank wall of refusal, despite the offer of the Marquess of Northampton to give the necessary land. And there at Kelly Bray the line has ever since stayed. The total cost of building the new link and converting the old line was put by Venning at £180,000[11].

EARLY DAYS

At first people were slow in using the new railway. The trading profit for the first half-year was only £572 and in the second half-year this had dropped to £303, largely due to teething troubles in operating over a difficult terrain. This meant a dividend of only 1 per cent against a final 2¼ per cent paid by the narrow-gauge company. Four trains a day each way catered for mixed passenger and freight traffic with four- and six-wheel type coaching stock of London & South Western origin.* On Thursdays and Saturdays an extra train in each direction carried travellers on cheap day-return tickets for Devonport and Plymouth—tickets which today cost 5s but in 1908 were 1s 8d and 1s 10d. Goods could still be sent to Plymouth more cheaply by barge, though the barges were often difficult to collect and were sometimes weatherbound for days. The trains were regular and usually punctual. By 1913 the railway's superiority was established, 112,639 passengers being carried in that year and a dividend of 3½ per cent paid—½ per cent more than the previous year. Dreams of reaching into north Cornwall centred on a 7-mile extension, planned in 1909 from the Callington road terminus to a junction with the North Cornwall line near Launceston. A light railway order was obtained for this in February of that year but the time limit expired and the project lapsed. (In the 1920s a further scheme to extend the line to Five Lanes, near Altarnun, also lapsed through lack of support.)

Three engines had been specially built for the new line. Two were 0-6-2 tanks named *Earl of Mount Edgecumbe* and *Lord St Levan*, while the third, *A. S. Harris*, named after the first secretary of the

---

* Passenger coaches, until diesel trains arrived, usually consisted of two of the former LSW 25-ton centre-gangway railcar trailers built for the Plymouth suburban service in 1904.

company, was an o-6-o tank. They originally had a blue livery with
red lining and brass steam domes and chimney caps. At Bere Alston
they ran into the outer face of the platform which adjoins the main
Waterloo line, thus allowing through services and vehicles to be
exchanged with the South Western; the link with the Mineral Railway was made with an end-on connection between Gunnislake and
Calstock at a point where the original track heads off to the now-
abandoned incline. The rudimentary semaphore signals of the old
Mineral Railway were replaced by an interlocking system designed
for passenger traffic, although between Bere Alston and Calstock a
train staff was used. The line was single track except for crossing
loops and at stations.

   Not being a passenger line, the Mineral Railway contented itself
with depots. With the line's new status these were upgraded, Calstock, Gunnislake and Latchley Halt becoming stations. Stoke
Climsland became Luckett station on 1 November 1909, and won
fame for its 'smart and trim station mistress', who attended single-
handed to parcels, passengers and goods. An additional station at
Chilsworthy designed to meet the heavy mineral and passenger
traffic from industries immediately north of Gunnislake opened on
1 June 1909. The terminus at Kelly Bray enjoyed the name of
Callington Road, following the time-honoured South Western habit
of adding 'Road' to any station from which passengers were faced
with a lengthy walk to the town it was supposed to serve. This was
shortened to Callington for Stoke Climsland in November 1909 and
remained so until the station's closure in 1966.

   To connect the goods sidings at Calstock with the riverside quays,
a wagon hoist for use alongside the viaduct was designed by Galbraith & Church and installed by Head, Wrightson & Company, the
foundations for it being taken out by Lang in 1907 while the viaduct
was building. This lift was one of the highest in the country and
unique in the West of England. A maximum load of 15 tons was
raised or lowered approximately 110 ft by a steam winding engine

powered by a locomotive-type boiler. Trucks from a siding at Calstock ran into a cage alongside the engine and were lowered directly on to a turntable on the quay, from where they were hauled away by horses.

THE LINE IN THE VALLEY'S LIFE

Without any connecting link with a main rail route the old Mineral Railway left the horticultural trade largely untouched, but for its successor the transit of fruit, and later of flowers, assumed more and more importance as the brick or granite industries declined. Between May and July 1908 up to 100 tons of strawberries were sent away in special trains made up at Gunnislake for despatch through to Exeter, whence they ran fast to Waterloo. The waiting rooms and platforms of the little wayside stations were heavy with the scent of the old Phoebe and Royal Sovereign varieties packed in 3-lb punnets.

As the years sped by to 1914 excursion traffic began to tax the line, especially during the summer. The company offered special rates to tourists and parties, who began in increasing numbers to discover a railway which offered dramatic river and moorland views and could be enjoyed without the handicap of sulphurous tunnels and industrial haze. On Hingston Down itself the enterprising James Venning had set up swing boats and facilities for boiling tea kettles, and in 1910 a halt was built at Seven Stones between Latchley and Luckett. To it flocked excursionists and school parties laden with picnic hampers, and a nostalgic reminder of this long-vanished traffic is the company's official time-table for June–September 1914, advertising five trains a day between Callington and Bere Alston and six on Sundays, with special facilities for holidaymakers, works parties, Bands of Hope and Sunday schools. It is a strange spot to visit today—bare and open to the four winds, the remains of a platform and a cottage marking the site of a halt that was never used after September 1917.

On 1 January 1923 the track became part of the Southern Railway, following the regrouping of the main-line companies, and the Plymouth Devonport & South West Junction Railway passed into history. Motor traffic was as yet an unimportant competitor and the guard could still board the train at Callington and collect £7 in fares by the time he had reached Bere Alston.

Under the Southern, the railhead at Kelly Bray throughout the 1920s and 30s became increasingly important as a distribution and collecting centre for a wide area of farmland. Electricity replaced oil lamps and the single platform was extended to accommodate a four-coach train. Three sidings served the goods traffic which rolled across Calstock viaduct over a river empty of barges. The fruit traffic of the pre-1914 war years increasingly gave place to consignments of flowers. Calstock sent away between ten and fifteen vans a day when this was at its height, handling, with its neighbour Gunnislake, nearly 200,000 packages of fruit and flowers with lesser amounts from Callington and Luckett. Milk traffic grew, Gunnislake becoming an important collecting centre, but mining and arsenic production had largely ceased while the trade in bricks and terra-cotta tiles slumped so severely that only one works at Chilsworthy was producing them. The decline of the brick and granite trade and the absence of river cargoes diminished the usefulness of the steam lift. By 1930 the cost of manning it (a duty often performed by the locomotive drivers) was out of all proportion to its use and it was dismantled and sold for scrap in October 1934.

WAR AND NATIONALIZATION

Until 1939 over 15,000 passengers a year were regularly using a line which took them from Callington to Bere Alston station in

Derelict water-wheel at Devon Great Consols mine before its removal for scrap about the time of the last war. The wheel, about 25 ft in diameter, worked an arsenic grinding mill

Arsenic flue at Gawton. In places over 6 ft high and 2 ft thick, this flue constructed in the 1890s was claimed to be the longest of its kind in the country

Gill & Bray's foundry at Tavistock, probably the oldest foundry building in the town and dating from the early years of the nineteenth century. Now a storehouse, it was until a few years ago a wool-combing factory

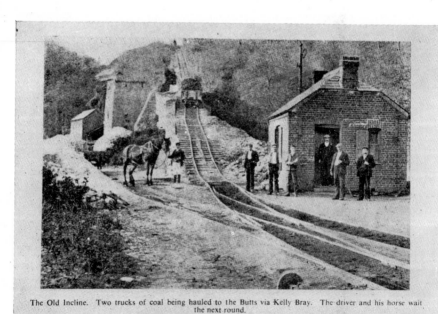

The Old Incline. Two trucks of coal being hauled to the Butts via Kelly Bray. The driver and his horse wait the next round.

The old wire rope incline from Calstock quay, disused after 1908. Two trucks of coal are being hauled up the incline. The horse was used for pulling trucks along the quay

forty minutes. Then came the war years; the population of the area, already swollen with evacuees from London, increased by as much as a third again as people fled from homes and streets in Plymouth and Devonport left stricken and burning by German bombers. The responsibility for transporting a huge surplus population to and from an area where even fowl houses were snapped up as temporary living accommodation fell almost entirely on a branch railway originally built to transport minerals. The scenes at Bere Alston station in 1941 as the 7.05 train waited double-headed to begin its nightly journey to Calstock, Gunnislake, Luckett and Callington resembled those of a main-line terminus rather than a country junction. Extra train crews were called in to work the Adams 0-4-4 tanks which did almost all the passenger haulage.

This landmark in the line's history looks all the more arresting when compared with the swift decline which followed. By 1945 the evacuees and the refugees from battered Plymouth were back in their homes, leaving the lonely and windswept stations strangely silent. Five years later nationalization handed the branch to the Western Region—a change surely permeated with irony, for the Great Western, as the forerunner of the Western region, now gained by Parliamentary decree a railway which served country it had pointedly ignored 100 years earlier as being too barren for development. Economically the horticultural traffic was of more importance than passengers, who averaged little more than 1,000 a week. During the war many of the bulb and fruit fields had been ploughed up, but immediately after 1945 the flower industry staged a remarkable recovery. In the 1950 season, twenty-one special trains representing nearly 600 vans were being despatched from Gunnislake, and even small stations like Luckett became receiving depots for 900 boxes of flowers and almost 5½ tons of fruit. Ten years later (1959–60 season) Calstock was sending away 268 tons of fruit and Gunnislake rivalled Bere Alston with despatches of 80 tons of flowers and 32,000 chips of fruit.

o

Through all these changes the branch had remained faithful to steam, but on 5 September 1964 the shrill toot of steam whistles at the level crossings was heard for the last time. On 7 September came the first diesel locomotive, celebrating the occasion by breaking down at Gunnislake and making the dockyard workers it carried one and a half hours late. The diesels replaced Midland tanks, which in 1953 had taken over from the original gallant little Hawthorne Leslie engines, *Lord St Levan* and *Earl Mount Edgcumbe*[12]. These had given forty-five years of continuous service and in peak periods were in traffic for ten hours or more a day. Because of maintenance requirements they were seldom on the line together in later years. Their small wheels, which gave them better adhesion on the steep gradients and curves, suited them for the lion's share of the goods work on a branch that not only had its running line but most of its sidings on gradients; slipping wheels were a hazard even with these engines. Although there were check rails, autumn leaves and mists made the track particularly treacherous through the Harewood cutting, and throughout the life of the branch the working rule was that all goods trains over this section had to be accompanied by a heavy wagon with sanding gear.

The blueprint for the future of Britain's railways made no provision for a branch line ending on a windy granite ridge. Goods trains ceased to run between Gunnislake and Callington in the autumn of 1965 and passenger trains a year later. Thus a story which began with a ceremonial cutting of turf in 1863 to provide a railway to Callington ended on Saturday, 5 November 1966 with Callington again isolated from the railway it so earnestly sought.

The remainder of the South Western story in the Tamar Valley is a compound of loss and precarious survival. Because there is no adequate road in the eastern half of the valley (providing one would probably exceed the cost of the original $22\frac{1}{2}$ miles of main line between Lydford and Plymouth) a brisk morning and evening commuter traffic has ensured the retention, for the time being, of the

rail link between Plymouth and Gunnislake, and with it Calstock's
graceful viaduct. But north from Bere Alston to Okehampton there
is now a railway void—the lines ripped up, stations derelict—only
the link between Meldon and Okehampton remains and that is in
doubt. Tavistock North station lost its goods traffic in 1965 and a
year later suffered cuts in its passenger traffic. The end of the old
South Western main line in the valley came on a wet Sunday night
(5 May 1968) when the last passenger train ran through to Plymouth. Thus Tavistock which once had two stations (the GWR
Southern station was closed from 31 December 1962) now has
none. All the valley fruit traffic now goes by lorry for marshalling at
Plymouth—a traffic which in the old South Western and Southern
days was largely rail borne and largely marshalled at Bere Alston
where, in the spring and summer, the destination cards on the
freight trucks read like a roll-call of the fruit, flower and vegetable
markets of London, the Midlands and the North.

The South Western's main line into Plymouth through the Tamar
Valley has often been cited as an example of needless railway dupli-
cation. But in the climate of the 1890s there were good reasons for
building it. It helped an important agricultural area around Bere
Alston which was untouched and ignored by the Great Western,
and it improved suburban services. Above all it brought competition. The rivalry between the two companies for the Tamar Valley
fruit trade had an intensity and excitement difficult to appreciate
today and this dramatically stimulated the flagging industry.

On the debit side the South Western finally ended the long and
picturesque history of the Tamar as a commercial highway. But
without a drastic improvement at prohibitive cost of the road approaches to its quays, the river with its tricky channel and in-
convenient tides was doomed anyway with the dawn of the twentieth
century.

CHAPTER TWELVE

The Vale of Plenty

THE dividing line between industry and agriculture in the Tamar Valley is difficult to draw. The two are almost as old as each other and have existed side by side over several hundred years. Industrial processes have mingled and interlocked with the cultivation of the soil, and the two have played vital and alternating roles in its economy. A few dozen yards from the abandoned mine or quarry with its shafts and dumps, there is more often than not the gnarled cherry tree split and deformed with age, or the half-forgotten clearing where strawberries and spring flowers were once cultivated. Between them they have brought almost as much wealth to the Valley as the mines and have employed almost as many people. Today the market garden industry brings in over £750,000 a year, and it has a history no less fascinating than that of the mines, brick-making plants and quarries it has supplanted.

On land with slopes as steep as 34 degrees and where plots have gradients of 1 in 1 and 1 in 2, agriculture develops a special character. Mechanical ingenuity is as important as agricultural expertise in evolving ploughing methods, for instance. An old truck or car is driven by a circular route to the top of the plot and a wooden axle fixed to take the drive from the engine. From this a wire rope is led to the bottom of the plot and attached to the plough. From the stationary car, which is often managed by the wife, the drive from the engine pulls the plough to the top guided by the husband. Industrial craft is also seen in the use of agricultural tools seldom noticed elsewhere. These include not only the turning fork and long-handled Cornish shovel, but the curiously named sclum (similar to a manure drag) and the Tamar Valley dibber. This is a tool with a narrow blade set at rather more than a right angle to the short handle, designed to make vertical holes on steeply sloping ground.

The situation and climate of the Tamar Valley make it nearly perfect for fruit and flower growing and it produces crops a week to a fortnight earlier than any district east of Cornwall. The summer visitor hurrying across the Tamar by car or train to the coast sees little of this industry carried on among steep, hidden valleys and in moist, fertile plots and fields lying at the end of age-old lanes and trackways. Probably not more than 700 growers are concerned with it on the Cornish side and they are to be found in a strip of country about 8 miles long and scarcely a mile wide in the parishes of Stoke Climsland, Calstock, St Dominic and Landulph. On the Devon side the area includes the whole of the Bere Alston peninsula down to the water meadows bordering the Tavy at Tamerton Foliot.

The fields and valleys making up this rich market-garden countryside almost always border the river or its tributaries. Protected from the north and east winds, they have a rainfall of nearly 50 in, but are usually dry in the vital months of April, May and June. Summer temperatures can reach a steady 70 degrees and the steep south-facing slopes warm up rapidly. Everywhere there is the subtle, moist influence of the sea, while the river keeps down the menace of frost.

The area has long been famous for fruit growing. Cherries and cider apples have been grown in such abundance that visitors making the trip from Plymouth to Calstock in the late eighteenth and early nineteenth centuries had the impression of travelling through one vast fruit garden. Unlike the cherries of the eastern counties, which are probably crossed with a French stock, the black Tamar Valley cherry is native to the area and was probably the earliest fruit grown on anything resembling a commercial scale. In the eighteenth century the trees grew in haphazardly planted orchards whose neglected appearance would astound a modern fruit grower, with his orderly plantations and careful spraying programme. Like the cattle of the time they were left to fend for themselves, appreciated only for what they produced. Pruning was seldom attempted, spraying almost unknown, and the crowded boughs and branches were swathed in a cocoon-like mass of waving grey lichen. Nor were the cider-apple orchards any better, the trees deep in nettles and docks with pigs rooting among them.

Blossom time hid these defects and it was the sight of cherry trees in bloom on either side of the Tamar and the extraordinary variety of fruit grown in the moist valley bottoms that caught and held the attention of earlier travellers. Marshall in 1796 found Bere Ferrers a centre 'where cherries, pears, walnuts are raised in great abundance for local markets', and he estimated 'that all of a thousand pounds worth of fruit, including strawberries' was sent out annually from the neighbourhood.

The historian Polwhele was surprised at the cherry crop. Lysons commented on the abundance of orchards in Calstock and Stoke Climsland and appears to have acquired a taste for Tamar Valley cider, 'a rich strong-bodied liquor, equal to the best cider of the South Hams'. It was made from the 'dufflin' apple, a variety now almost extinct, which produced a medium-bodied cider probably not to present-day taste[1]. In the closing years of the eighteenth century, as the market garden of Plymouth and of its growing naval satellite town of Dock, Tamar Valley produce substantially contributed to the £616 a year which Lord St Aubyn received in tolls from Devonport Market.

The highly organized marketing industry one sees in the Tamar Valley today, however, is a child of the reforms in agricultural methods forced upon nineteenth-century landowners, farmers and growers by the legacy of land neglect during the Napoleonic wars.

At the beginning of the war with France much of the Tamar Valley and the land around it was worked on an age-old cropping system aided by sea sand and 'beat burning', which conserved the soil well enough for an agricultural economy that had altered little since feudal times, but was ill-adapted to face the needs of a war whose blockades almost overnight caused an urgent demand for wheat and fodder from home sources. Wheat prices jumped from 47s 7d a quarter in the decade before the outbreak of war to 113s 10d in 1800, and were to reach 126s 6d in 1812. Farmers and landowners everywhere put every acre they could find under straw crops, ruthlessly plundering the land to produce a 'ruinous rotation' in which barley and wheat predominated. Fertility was sucked out of the soil. By 1808 Vancouver was noting that the 'thin grey loam' around Bere Ferrers was already much impoverished by a succession of white straw crops. Towards the end of the war the upland areas around Bere Ferrers, containing some of the finest corn land in West Devon, nearly went out of cultivation, so exhausted were they by frequent tillage. Much market-garden land was in little better plight.

Nursing the soil back to fertility after the peace was a laborious process, only slowly achieved by a combination of new cropping methods, improved farm techniques and artificial manures made available by new industrial processes. A start was made from 1815 onwards in West Devon and Cornwall by greatly increasing the acreage under turnips, a crop which previously had been indifferently grown, although it was being widely cultivated in eastern England. Turnips, by providing better winter feed for cattle, indirectly increased the fertility of the soil, and the early days of June saw dense clouds of smoke overhang the fields as farmers beat-burned the earth as part of the 'grand preparation' for planting the crop.

Then improved grinding machinery made bone flour and dust more readily available, and this was first introduced into the area in 1835 with magical results on the phosphate-hungry soils; the results of one application were frequently noticeable for ten years afterwards. Bone-grinding mills appeared on the Tamar, and barges with cargoes of bones imported from France became a familiar sight on the river. The remains of one mill worked by a water-wheel can still be seen by the river's edge at Cargreen.

The rise of the gas industry made gas lime (especially valuable on recently reclaimed land) and sulphate of ammonia readily available at Plymouth. Large stocks were held at Halton Quay, where phosphates, advertised as the best fertilizer for turnips, could be bought for £7 10s a ton. By 1850 a whole range of artificial manures, along with Chilean nitrates and guano, and phosphate of soda, were readily available in the neighbourhood. Not everybody took kindly to them: when Samuel Crump, who farmed at Kingston, near Plymouth, was complimented on an outsize crop of turnips, he took the opportunity to announce that he had grown them with old-fashioned dung and oarweed (seaweed), which he much preferred to phosphate of soda.

The plough was improved after 1815, enabling it to penetrate deeper beneath the growan top soils. Societies sprang up to foster competition, among them the East Cornwall Agricultural Society founded at Callington in 1863. This yearly show became a shop window for Tamar Valley growers, until between the two world wars their more specialized needs earned their own horticultural show—which had a humble beginning on a vicarage lawn. A land-reclamation programme started in the previous century on marshes between Plymouth and the Tavy estuary was resumed over a hundred years later by the Earl of Mount Edgcumbe at Bere Alston and St Dominic. Here his agent, by the liberal application of gas lime, grew crops of mangolds and corn which were reckoned to return 4 per cent on the capital invested in reclaiming the land.

In Landulph, Calstock and St Dominic, where soils tended to be light over the slates and shales, farmers with holdings averaging about 100 acres were cutting 18 bushels of wheat an acre, 26 of barley, 42 of oats and 1 to 1½ tons of hay. Kidney potatoes were extensively grown (it was customary to prepare land for wheat by growing a 'large breadth' of potatoes) and some 16,000 tons sent annually to Covent Garden. Perhaps the most significant change of all since the beginning of the century had been the increase in the variety of green crops, whose previous deficiency had been one of the biggest defects of husbandry in the area. In 1810 vetches and carrots were scarcely to be seen; forty years later they were in general cultivation along with sanfoin, rape, cabbages and mangolds.

The step from the improvement of field produce to better market-garden and fruit supplies was a short and logical one. By the middle of the century growers in the Tamar Valley were actively experimenting with fruit crops. The first small and tentative trials were hampered by a lack of markets; Plymouth and Devonport were the only large centres of population, and Plymouth by 1850 had little more than 50,000 people. Strawberries in Devonport market at that time were fetching only 6d a lb, and sometimes as little as $1\frac{1}{2}$d, while cherries sold for 2d and 3d a lb. The real breakthrough came with the arrival of the railway in Plymouth in 1849. The more forward-looking growers began to think of supplying distant markets with early fruit: this could be picked one day on the Tamar's banks and be on sale in Covent Garden the next.

The cherry orchards, which the earlier travellers and historians had so much admired, were among the first to benefit. At Botus Fleming—the cherry village—and St Dominic, growers in the middle of last century were grafting old varieties on to the wild cherry, which was used as a rootstock. Some fifteen new sorts were thus produced, mostly named after the farms of their origin. Only three of these varieties now survive in any quantity—Burcombe, an early cherry first raised at Burcombe Farm and now mainly sold locally for bottling, Birchenhayes and Fice, the latter raised on a St Dominic farm and generally regarded as the best flavoured of all the Tamar Valley cherries.

They grew (and still do in isolated clumps) on huge trees not uncommonly 50 ft high, often needing 60-ft ladders to pick them. Small, black and very sweet, these dessert Tamar cherries are earlier than the Kentish varieties and not so prone to split in wet weather. In their heyday their yields were tremendous, 7–10 cwt often being taken from a tree; picking began soon after the strawberry crop. Until the first world war the cherry trees on both sides of the valley yielded 30 or more tons a year and were a source of mingled delight and astonishment to visitors. The scene in the spring at Botus Fleming and St Dominic, and in the country around Bere Alston, was breathtaking in its fragile beauty. Great drifts of blossom weaved and rumpled in the wind like an undulating carpet of pink and white snow. One huge tree at Bere Ferrers is said to have yielded 1,000 lb of fruit.

In 1856 the crop was worth 'all of £200 a year', the fruit being sold throughout the country at 2d and 5d a pound. Cherry orchards (or gardens as they were more often called) formed the more valuable part of most worthwhile farm property in the area and were specially mentioned in auctioneers' advertisements. Pentillie had a cherry feast, huge cherry pies being cooked in the kitchens of Pentillie House and slices distributed to the children of neighbouring parishes; the custom died at the end of the century.

Although much of the crop found its way to Plymouth, London and the Midlands were important markets, and the produce of the Tamar cherry orchards was still regarded as sufficiently important during the first world war for pinnace-loads of sailors to be sent from Devonport barracks to help in picking. This no longer happens: few trees have been planted in the last forty years. Labour is scarce and expensive and few people are willing to mount and handle the huge ladders. With ageing trees the yield is freakish, for while an exceptional year may still produce 10 or 12 tons, of which 8 might go to up-country markets, three or four years may pass without the crop being worth gathering. The white glory that once covered the Tamar Valley in spring time is now mainly confined to a few straggling orchards around Botus Fleming and Halton Quay, and some isolated trees at Bere Alston.

The development of the strawberry trade arose not so much from the raising of new varieties as from the ability of the new railway to carry the fruit quickly to Covent Garden. Platefuls of plump, red glistening early strawberries, ideally topped with a mound of clotted cream, are the Tamar Valley's contribution to the joys of the table— through the railway they became obtainable far beyond Devon and Cornwall. They brought almost overnight a new source of livelihood, a firm alternative to the failing mines. Men sought out every available south-facing slope of land, and localities like Strawberry Hill at St Mellion have been identified with growing the fruit ever since. Strawberries remain today the second most important crop in the valley, between 300 and 400 tons being produced a year from about 300 acres. London and other markets take about three-quarters of the crop and the railway, as seen in the last chapter, is still the best means of transporting it.

The man who first found a market in London for Tamar Valley strawberries 100 years ago was James Walter Lawry, a tenant farmer in the Bohetherick Valley, St Dominic. Lawry had gone to London early in June 1863 to visit the International Exhibition. Looking in at Covent Garden he astonished salesmen by telling them he had been picking strawberries for a fortnight or more. He had a pressing invitation to send some up. The first small pilot lots consigned to London by train were unsatisfactory, mainly because they were poorly packed and had been gathered in the rain—a hazard which still frustrates growers. So Lawry visited Glasgow to learn to make white-wood punnets and returned to pass on his knowledge. Within three years Tamar Valley strawberries had become established in London and Midland markets, selling at 2s 6d per lb.

The strawberry is a shallow-rooting plant demanding a richly nourished soil. The crops in Lawry's time drew their abundance from the inherent fertility of the soil of freshly cleared oak coppice. But this was soon exhausted, and in their search for a cheap bulk manure the growers turned to the streets of Plymouth. Here their needs were met by 'dock dung', which was laid like a carpet over the strawberry beds at the lavish rate of 30 to 40 tons an acre with seaweed added for potash. It produced staggering yields. From St Dominic alone came between 200 and 300 tons of strawberries a year grown on beds remaining prolific for twenty years or more. The 'dock dung' was an evil-smelling compound of the sweepings of Plymouth and Devonport streets, fish waste, butchers' offal and night soil, daily accumulated in a huge heap at Pottery Quay, Devonport, and which could be taken away for the cost of transport.

It was transported up river in 40 to 50 ton barges, each barge representing about eight or nine horseloads, and frequently contained money swept up unnoticed from the city streets by which many a farm worker found himself a few shillings richer. The penalty for the fertility brought was a smell so strong throughout the valley that even the sober members of the Geological Survey complained in 1907 that pure country air in the Tamar Valley had for many years been 'mythical'. The use of dock dung was stopped by the sanitary authorities in 1913 and no substitute as good has been found.

The strawberry-growing pioneers used the early cropping variety Princess Maud, which has long vanished. But there were other varieties like Caroline and Phoebe, rich in colour, scent and taste, which older people still remember. In 1883 experiments were made in cleared woodland at Denham on the banks of the Tavy with a then new variety Royal Sovereign. The Denham experiment was so successful that this superb variety was planted throughout the Valley, the Bere peninsula rivalling the Cornish bank in production. From Saltash station alone 80 tons were sent to London in a single season and for 1s people were allowed in the fields to pick as much as they liked. A later variety, Paxton (named after the designer of the Crystal Palace), was planted to extend the picking period, and the two reigned supreme until the first world war, bringing the district almost legendary fame.

Women pickers started at the end of May for 1s 3d a day or 15s a week. They were out at first light, and it was the task of one picker in every ten to gather the bracken with which the round punnets of the day (made on kitchen tables in the winter for 1s a gross) were packed to cushion the fruit and keep it cool.

The St Dominic, Calstock and Bere Alston growers supplied mainly for the up-country markets and this made Cotehele quay one of the busiest spots in the valley towards the end of last century. Here on the long summer evenings early in June would gather the horse-drawn wagons, coming slowly from the fields piled high with boxes of fruit, whose scent on the evening air is still remembered by older people. At Cotehele the strawberries were ferried across to the Devon side at a cost of 1d a box to waiting horse-drawn railway vans.

In retrospect the period 1860–1914 appears as the time of plenty for the horticultural industry in the Tamar Valley. As the prolific beds around St Dominic became exhausted, production shifted farther down the valley to the St Mellion area, but the yields were still as high. The demand for land for fruit purposes doubled rents. Although harvesting costs amounted to 25 per cent of the crop, labour and materials were abundant and cheap, and disease well controlled.

This progress was abruptly halted by the first world war and the industry's attempts at revival after 1918 took place in a different world. Virus diseases struck plants and soils weakened by long bearing with all the virulence of the biblical plagues. Red core and eelworm destroyed whole plantations of strawberries and dozens of fields became empty. The succulent Royal Sovereign proved so susceptible to the virus-bearing aphis to which the strawberry plant is a host that it disappeared from the fields and has never been grown in quantity in the Valley since. Since those days the story of strawberry growing in the Tamar Valley, as elsewhere, is of one long search for a plant resistant to disease. The industry, with the help of the Ellbridge experimental station at Saltash, has been built up anew with varieties like Favourite, Prizewinner and Vigour, good commercial strains but without the flavour of Royal Sovereign. Today growers in an average season send between 2,000 and 3,000 $\frac{1}{2}$-lb punnets a day to London, Bristol, Manchester and Glasgow. In 1906 it was estimated that the annual output of strawberries in the Tamar Valley was between 200 and 300 tons a year. Present-day production, achieved on much less acreage, compares not unfavourably with the golden virus-free years of the turn of the century. But the business has to fight resourceful competitors, as well as disease: airborne consignments of strawberries come from France, California and New Zealand, and probably soon from Japan. Much work has been done to bring the Tamar plants into bearing even earlier in the season, when prices are highest. Whether James Lawry would think the modern strawberries tasted as well as those with which he first astonished Covent Garden is another question.

It was in the late spring of 1880 that a few stallholders in Devonport market rather nervously displayed for sale some double-white narcissi. They had been noticed growing wild in the hedgerows near Clamoake Farm, Bere Alston, and the farmer, a Mr Jackson, entranced with their heady perfume, sent a few bunches for sale as a speculation.

In this way the Tamar Valley flower industry was born; its considerable value today growers are shy of estimating. Birthdays, festivals, 'dates', anniversaries—all the social conventions of an affluent age increasingly demand flowers, and today flower growing in the Tamar Valley earns more money and occupies more acres than does fruit.

The disease and virus plagues which followed the end of the 1914 war proved as devastating among the bulb fields as in the fruit beds. From 1922 onwards the eelworm plague destroyed complete bulb fields and the whole of the narcissi-growing industry virtually came to a standstill. A precariously balanced economy faced ruin. The eelworm, which harbours in the crown of the bulb, was eventually controlled by what has become known as the 'hot water treatment', a method devised and perfected in the Tamar Valley by which bulbs before planting are steamed for three hours at a temperature of 112 degrees and then treated with a mercury compound.

Some 350 acres in the Tamar Valley are now under bulb cultivation. A newcomer since the last war is the anemone, providing work and a valuable income between the daffodil and strawberry seasons, although this too has shown recent signs of disease. A marketing programme of daffodils, strawberries and anemones in that order is now the pattern of the industry and the dominance of flowers over fruit is seen from the following figures of railway loadings from Saltash and Bere Alston stations over the last seven years. The numbers refer to boxes:

Season	Flowers	Strawberries
1958–9	287,992	104,816
1959–60	219,973	73,108
1960–61	301,709	68,147
1961–2	192,060	83,363
1962–3	226,153	84,044
1963–4	272,102	80,007
1964–5	200,055	52,707

This pattern has been preserved as the industry enters the seventies, although in money terms strawberries are still the main economic crop of the Tamar Valley, accounting for over half of a total crop value which in a good year can be nearly £1,000,000.

Notes and References

1 The magazine *Devonia*, March 1907, mentions that the weaving of dress and other material was carried on for a few years in the Gunnislake neighbourhood 'but failed to be a success in consequence of being too far away from the source of the yarn which had to be brought from Yorkshire'.

2 The manor of Calstock was originally a gift of William the Conqueror. It was sold in 1806 to John Williams of Scorrier House, Cornwall. The manor was abolished in 1926.

3 John Taylor, the engineer of the Tavistock Canal, in his preface to the 1811 edition of Risdon's *Survey of Devonshire*, refers to the water-wheels in use at several copper mines near Tavistock as 'some of the most extensive and powerful engines in the world'.

4 There is a small outcrop of much-splintered granite at Frementor on the Devon bank of the Tamar just above Gunnislake. The rock structure of the Tamar Valley is more complicated than the brief reference indicates, and is so confused by small granite intrusions as to present a number of puzzles. No firm southern boundary has yet been found between the newer Carboniferous measures and the older Devonian rocks in the neighbourhood of Tavistock. In 1889 when the London & South Western Railway line between Lydford and Plymouth was being built, R. N. Worth, a Plymouth geologist, spent six months tramping up and down the newly excavated cuttings and tunnels, to the astonishment of navvies and labourers, with a hammer and notebook trying unsuccessfully to solve the problem. Worth's paper to the 1889 meeting of the Devonshire Association at Tavistock describing his search and conclusions is well worth reading.

5 *PDWJ*, 4 December 1851.

6 In September 1866 it was reported that a large number of men had gone from the Tavistock district to Essex and Kent to work on the railway, where they were promised 'certain employment for at least two years' (*WMN*, 18 September 1866). Uncertainty about the life of a mine was one of the biggest employment hazards of miners of the period.

7 See *PDWJ*, 20 April 1854, and *WMN*, 22 August 1864 and 13 August 1867. Between 1865 and 1867 poor relief in Calstock parish almost doubled, while the price of flour in two years advanced from 30s to 52s a sack. During that period an underground miner's wages had dropped

One of the original 0-4-0 East Cornwall Mineral Railway locomotives, a picture taken outside the smith's shop at the top of the incline

The four-coupled tank locomotive Hugo, *one of two engines working the Devon Great Consols railway from about 1880. This picture from the* Locomotive Magazine, *1903, was probably taken at an earlier date at the Cambrian Foundry, Wales, where the engine was being repaired*

Earl of Mount Edgcumbe and (above) A. S. Harris, two engines of the PD *&* SWR

Gunnislake station soon after the opening of the PD *&* SWR

from 65s a month to 54s 6d. Many families then made their own bread and it was estimated that a miner with a wife and six children consumed half a sack of flour a month.

CHAPTER TWO

1 The Tamar, 57½ miles long and having its source about 4 miles from Bude, has always been jealously regarded in Cornwall as a Cornish river, and Devon has made little effort to dispute the title.

2 These manganese mines, lying just outside the northern perimeter of the Tamar Valley, worked lodes which ran on an east–west strike for about 8 miles in the neighbourhood of Brentor. Many of the deposits were first found while ploughing or draining farmland. (See Thomas Newman, *History of Coryton*, 1940.)

3 The railway would have ended at Morwellham at a point east of the Ship Inn 'and at the lower or eastern quay or wharf'.

4 Mrs Rundle Charles, *Our Seven Homes*. Mrs Charles was the daughter of John Rundle, one of Tavistock's MPs.

5 For example Nicholas Bonde and John Sabton, who were barge owners in the fifteenth century.

6 See C. S. Gilbert's *Historical Survey of Cornwall*, which refers to the 'powerful hydraulic engines' (water-wheels) working this mine which could be seen on the river bank below Gunnislake.

7 Venning's *Postal Directory*, 1881. This was one of a number of publications sponsored by James Venning of Callington, whose campaigning for better communications and greater recognition of the importance of Callington as the centre of East Cornwall made him a vivid and well-known personality. His *Historical Notes*, published over intervals between 1901 and 1934, form a chaotic ragbag of useless and useful information from which occasional treasures can be dredged.

8 I am grateful to the late Prof A. H. Shorter of Exeter University for much of the information on the Danescombe Mill.

9 See *PDWJ*, 12 October 1854. Below this building, at Hatches Green, was a bone mill, and some elderly people in the neighbourhood still possess exquisitely carved fan, umbrella, knife and fork handles found in bone cargoes which came from ivory and bone-carving districts of France.

10 The tax, first imposed in 1784, averaged 4s 7d a thousand on ordinary bricks; on special bricks it was still more. (*Encyclopedia Britannica*, 11th edition; article on bricks.)

11 See *WMN*, 16 April 1873. The development seems to have started in 1870 by a firm with a capital of £200,000, who 'are combining brick burning, metal smelting and the extraction of the mineral oils from shales

P

and the manufacture of bitumen, asphalt and other substances'. This was presumably the West of England Fireclay, Bitumen & Chymical [*sic*] Company, whose works were at Dimson, above Gunnislake, and later expanded into the Greenhill arsenic works. The brickmaking industry on Hingston Down was aided by the construction of the East Cornwall Mineral Railway; one firm finding horse transport too costly had bought a traction engine which took a load of over 10 tons 'up the steepest hills at a rate of 3 to 4 miles an hour'.

12 *WDM*, 14 April 1875.

13 The Tamar Firebrick Company was in liquidation two years later, but its capital was reorganized and it resumed production as the West of England Firebrick Company with a number of orders for 'the Dockyard, Cardiff and other places' (*WDM*, 14 April and 10 August 1875). Although much has been destroyed, chiefly when the stack was toppled for safety reasons in the 1930s, the main outline of this factory can be clearly traced.

14 Westlake's former brickworks at Calstock now makes containers for the fruit trade. Westlake was one of the first people in Calstock to have a telephone, his Calstock and Rumleigh factories being connected.

15 *WDM*, 20 June 1864.

16 I am indebted to Mr Michael Bouquet of Bampton, Tiverton, for particulars about the registration of the *Tamar Queen*. She was launched in the Tamar at 7.30 a.m. on a Monday morning and despite the time over 200 people watched 'as the beautiful vessel slid off the slip to the waters of our unrivalled Tamar in splendid time' (*WDM*, 16 and 20 December 1864).

17 Over 2,000 trees were blown down on the estate in this storm of 9 March 1891.

18 The *Garlandstone* was reported to be in Barry Docks in 1964 waiting to be taken to America, but I have been unable to trace her since.

19 When this granite had to be cut to widen Gunnislake Hill about two years ago, it proved to be so hard that the County Council had to extend by another two months the time allotted for the work.

20 Another (and smaller) quarry below this, Snowden's quarry, specialized in granite setts and blocks for streets, gutters and road channels. It also supplied the granite ballast for the piers of the London & South Western Railway viaduct over the Tavy.

CHAPTER THREE

Material for the early part of this chapter has been obtained from G. R. Lewis, *The Stannaries*, Salzmann, *English Industries in the Middle Ages* and Finberg, *The Stannary of Tavistock, TDA*, Vol. LXXXI, 1949. Most of the information about Johnson and the Tamar Consols mine has been derived from

Notes and References

Donald McDonald's memoir, *Percival Norton Johnson*, 1951, of which a copy was kindly given me by the author. The output figures of the mines in the nineteenth century are those of the 1921 Geological Survey report by Dewey on lead, silver-lead and zinc ores.

1 The Bere Alston peninsula is largely composed of Carboniferous slates and it is only in these slates that the lead and silver-lead ores are fully developed. Directly they approach the adjoining granite in the north the lodes became barren.

2 It is often overlooked that the Combe Martin and Bere mines seem to have been discovered, abandoned and then reworked over roughly comparable periods, although separated from each other by over 40 miles. The deposits have certain features in common. In the thirteenth and fourteenth centuries the yield from the Bere mines probably exceeded those of Combe Martin (see W. J. Prew, 'On Metals in Devon', *TDA*, Vol. LXXXI, 1949).

3 The church received a certain amount of 'tithe ore' from the mines. In 1297 this was being bought back from the rector of Bere at 2s a load, 9d being deducted from that sum for washing the ore.

4 The ore was laid on a thick bed of tan ash. When fired a blast was turned on to the upper surfaces of the molten metal which was then rapidly oxidized (Salzmann).

5 *TDA*, Vol. XVI.

6 In 1851, when the mines were most prosperous, Bere Alston had a population of 3,400, of which over 1,000 were employed in the mines. It then had three schools, nine dressmakers, four shoemakers, four wheelwrights, eleven shopkeepers, two millers and three bakers.

7 Smelting seems to have been carried on at the works until about 1856. In 1853 two plates of silver weighing 11,704 oz are noted as the production of two weeks' smelting at the Tamar works, and other similar pieces of plate are reported as being produced in June and July. The Tamar works were particularly adapted for smelting low-grade ore.

8 *PDWJ*, 4 September 1856, in a report headed 'Distressing inundation and immense loss of property'. It was noted that the entire neighbourhood was almost wholly dependent on the mines.

9 *WMN*, 27 March 1861.

CHAPTER FOUR

The references to Tavistock Abbey and to the early cost and carriage of sea sand are taken from Professor H. P. R. Finberg's *Tavistock Abbey*. Use has also been made of an article on the use of sea sand and limestone by N. J. G. Pounds in Volume XXII of *Devon & Cornwall Notes & Queries*, and R. G.

Stanes's transcription of Samuel Colepresse's 'A Georgicall Survey of Devon and Cornwall', *TDA*, Vol. XCVI. The references to 'Marshall' are to William Marshall's *The Rural Economy of the West of England*, 1796, Volumes 1 and 2.
1   Limestone occurs in thin beds at Lifton, but according to S. Baring-Gould, *Early Reminiscences*, pp. 5 and 247, its existence was unknown until the eighteenth century.
2   'An account of the lime rocks of the neighbourhood', *South Devon Monthly Museum*, Vol. 1, January to June 1833. See also R. N. Worth, 'Limestone Rocks of Plymouth', *TPI*, Vol. 5, p. 1. A more recent account of these deposits is given in C. J. R. Braithwaite's *Middle Devonian Sedimentation*, a copy of which is in the Plymouth Reference Library. The best limestone was said to have come from the now-disused Stonehouse quarries, to be seen at the back of Richmond Wharf.
3   London, 1798.
4   *PDWJ*, 7 May 1849.
5   Between 1819 and 1870 over 244,000 tons of limestone were carried over the Tavistock Canal.
6   This information was kindly supplied by Ald Fred Rogers, of St Dominic, whose firm burned lime at Halton Quay from about 1909 and was the last to use the kilns.

CHAPTER FIVE

1   H. E. Carrington, *The Plymouth and Devonport Guide*, 1830. Carrington was the son of the poet.
2   *PDWJ*, 20 June 1822, gives the following dimensions for the *Sir Francis Drake*: 150 tons, length 100 ft, breadth 18 ft, depth 12 ft, two engines of 25 hp, cost £500.
3   *WB*, 28 May 1824.
4   *PDWJ*, 25 July 1850.
5   *Plymouth and South Devon Monthly Museum*, 1 March 1833.
6   *PDWJ*, 1 September 1853.
7   *PDWJ*, 22 August 1850.
8   *PDWJ*, 18 September 1856.
9   *PDWJ*, 16 October 1856.
10   *PDWJ*, 25 September 1856. The rival company lasted less than two years, notices for its voluntary winding up appearing in January 1858.
11   In the *WMN* and *WDM* advertisements for 'Rowe's pleasant trips' appear almost every day in the summer from 1864 until the 1870s. The trips were frequently noticed in the news columns of the two papers from which the quoted extracts are taken.
12   *PDWJ*, 20 April 1854.

13 *PDWJ*, 25 May 1854. It was much the same on the Devon side of the river. In Bere Alston during the cholera epidemic of 1849 scarcely a house had a closet, while cesspools were sited next to domestic wells. Eight or nine people of both sexes often slept together in a room. Overcrowding, the absence of drains and lack of a good water supply led to scenes in Tavistock 'revolting to humanity and many husbands are now driven to the pot house in consequence'. (See *PDWJ*, 13 September 1849 and 20 April 1854.)

14 McBryde's *Guide to Sea and River Trips in the Neighbourhood of Plymouth*.

15 She was built in Berlin in 1922 and originally named *Manna*.

CHAPTERS SIX AND SEVEN

The minutes of the committee supervising the construction of the Tavistock Canal and the early dues books are deposited at the Devon County Record office and these have been extensively drawn on. The *Mining Journal*, 11 April 1863, has yielded information about Taylor's reading in preparation for the building of the canal.

1 The place name 'Orestocks' along the road from Rock to Bere Alston recalls this traffic. At a point where three roads meet is a rough triangle of ground where packhorses dumped ore from mines in the Tamar Valley. It was allowed to accumulate and then taken by wagons to Morwellham for shipment.

2 In 1801–10 nearly 31,000 tons of ore, worth £323,612, had been raised in the Tavistock area. 'In the last 20 years,' wrote John Taylor in 1817, 'this district has been the scene of very active exertions in the pursuit of mining and the most spirited efforts have been made for tracing the veins and instituting trials upon them for the discovery of their contents. On many of these losses have been heavy, but some have produced very large quantities of copper and have paid the adventurers very handsome profits.'

3 There were eight shafts on the line of the tunnel, two of which were for ventilation. The only one now open is Bray's shaft (63 fathoms), named after Col Bray, the Duke's agent; it can be seen in a field 400 yd east of Rock crossroads. The tunnel itself has a slight curve and the spot where the two halves were joined can be traced to within a few feet by the position of the shot holes drilled for blasting charges. The complete estimate for building the canal was £33,800 and a further £6,200 was included as 'money to be raised for driving on lodes discovered in the tunnel'. The costs of excavating the tunnel were estimated at £18,480. To this was added £1,000 'for sinking two shafts each of 50 fathoms at £10 a fathom'; £1,400 'for erecting a steam engine to draw water from the shafts'; £1,500 for 'expenses of engine in fuel for five years'; and £200

for ropes, tackle, etc; making a total of £22,580. The estimate of £7 a
fathom for driving the tunnel was soon exceeded and Vancouver (*State
of Agriculture in Devon*, 1808) was writing of the tunnel costing £14 a
fathom exclusive of shafts.

4 I can find no convincing evidence to support the story about French
prisoners of war. To bring them from Princetown, which was not used
until 1806, would have meant a march of two hours or more each way.
If they were housed near the canal there is no record of any expenditure
for them in the committee's careful accounts. By the time the tunnel was
completed the Napoleonic wars had been over three years.

5 'On the Ventilation of Mines with the Description of a New Machine for
that Purpose', a paper read to the British Association by John Taylor.

6 'Report on Railways in England 1826–7' by Carl von Oeynhausen and
Heinrich von Decken, translated by E. A. Forward and read at a meeting
of the Newcomen Society on 14 October 1953.

7 R. Hansford Worth, *TPI*, 8 March 1888.

8 Trials of this method in December 1854 'were more successful than the
most sanguine hopes of the projectors led them to expect' (*PDWJ*,
7 December 1854).

9 It was found by the late Frank Cloke, a well-known Tavistock mine
surveyor, who considered there were rich deposits of tin on the south-
eastern extension of the Wheal Crebor lodes.

CHAPTER EIGHT

The *Mining Journal*, founded 1845, is one of the chief sources of information
for the early history of Devon Great Consols mine. Between November 1864
and January 1865, however, *The Western Morning News* published a number
of articles on the mine's history, embodying much contained in the early
issues of the *Mining Journal*. These articles and the paper's reports of many
subsequent half-yearly meetings have been chiefly consulted for details.
Material has also come from J. C. Goodrich's well-documented study 'Devon
Great Consols: a Study in Victorian Mining Enterprise', *TDA*, Vol. XCVL.
D. B. Barton also deals with the mine in his *Historical Survey of the Mines
and Mineral Railways of East Cornwall and West Devon*, 1964. For arsenic
preparation, the chief source has been R. W. Toll's 'The Arsenic Industry in
the Tavistock District', *Mining Magazine*, August 1953. Very few photographs or drawings of the surface features of Devon Great Consols exist.
Search at the Board of Trade and at the Public Record Office has failed to
find any scale drawings of engine houses or plans of the arsenic refineries, nor
do these appear to exist among the Bedford papers in the Devon County
Record Office, Exeter.

1 London & Westcountry Chamber of Mines Records, 1901–03.
2 Charles Thomas, *Mining Fields of the West of England*, 1867.
3 The full lease giving permission to work the sett is dated 26 July 1844 (DCRO). See also DCNQ, Vol. XXX, part VII, July 1966.
4 *WMN*, 19 November 1864.
5 R. W. Toll, *WMN*, 3 December 1958.
6 The Duke's principal mineral agent, J. Gibson Martin, noted in December 1868: 'Had the Duke thought fit to work his own mineral ground he would have been the gainer of £982,842 19s 10d, in addition to £269,506 3s received in dues and premiums, making a total of £1,252,349 2s 10d, and doubtless if his grace could take the mines into his own hands at this time he could pay all the losses sustained and still realize a handsome profit; which clearly shows how little cause the mining company generally upon the estate have to complain of the rate of dues.' (Mining Record Book, Bedford Papers, DCRO.)
7 When the tolls for the Tavistock West Turnpike gate were auctioned for £1,170 in 1858 this was said to be '£540 less than the previous year arising from the fact of the Devon Great Consols ore being about to be conveyed by the new line of railway' (*PDWJ*, 18 November 1858).
8 This was, of course, from the dues received only from Devon Great Consols. It was also estimated in 1868 that the Duke had received a further £23,934 10s 10d 'from mining companies now extinct' (Mining Record Book, Bedford Records, DCRO).
9 The table is Thomas Spargo's, compiled from his *Statistics and Observations of the Mines of Cornwall*, 1865.
10 Bedford Records, DCRO.
11 The lease for arsenic working, dated 24 September 1866, laid down that the chambers and flues connected with the roasting kiln should be carried a distance (horizontally) of at least 600 ft before uniting with the stack. 'The section of the main chamber and first length of the flue being of the length of 90 ft shall be 12 ft in height and 6 ft wide. A reduction shall be allowed after the first length of the flue but no part shall be less than $4\frac{1}{2}$ ft by three ft wide. The walls of the chamber and flues shall be solidly built of the thickness of at least $2\frac{1}{2}$ ft of masonry where the flue is of the greatest dimension and nowhere less than 2 ft.

'The precipitation of the arsenic sulphur gasses and volatile substances which pass beyond the main flues and chambers shall be effected by means of water falls and showers.' To prevent fogs the stack had to be at least 120 ft high.
12 The likelihood of tin being found at depth in the southern part of the Devon Great Consols sett is still an open question. Collins, who regarded the liquidation of the Devon Great Consols company in 1901 as 'very unnecessary', thought tin was there, a view developed by C. F. Barclay

in a paper read to the Royal Geological Society of Cornwall (Vol. XVI, p. 157–76). Tin has been found in Wheal Frementor, a mine in the sett originally developed from an adit, and which lies in granite. In 1929 there was a proposal, abandoned through lack of capital, to work this mine by open-cast methods to recover tin and wolfram.

13 *Mining Journal*, 29 May 1880.

14 A different fate awaited the two locomotives. *Hugo* was under repair in South Wales when the mine closed and remained there. *Ada* was used in the construction of the Bere Alston–Callington branch line and also for a time on a projected light railway to link Merrivale quarries at Tavistock with the GWR Princetown branch, a project killed by the outbreak of war. She was sold to the Belgian government in 1915 for war work and ended her days in the fields of Flanders. (See *Locomotive Magazine*, 31 January 1903.)

15 Moses Bawden, 'Mines and Mining in the Tavistock District', *TDA*, 1914.

CHAPTER NINE

Locomotives and Rolling Stock

When the line was converted to standard gauge the two original engines were rebuilt (in 1907–08) as 0-4-2 tank engines by the addition of a pair of diminutive solid trailing wheels. The cost of converting both was £3,800. No. 1 was sold in 1909; No. 2 was bought by the Manhood & Selsey Tramway in 1912 and named *Hesperus*, and was scrapped in 1931. The line's rolling stock, when it passed to the PD & SWJ, consisted, in addition to the two engines, of 126 two- or three-plank open wagons, three brake vans and two service vehicles. All had centre-combined buffer couplings and side chains.

1 *WMN*, 23 November 1863.

2 *Journal of Transport History*, Vol. IV, No. 1, May 1959, pp. 21–2.

3 *PDWJ*, 6 January 1859.

4 *WMN*, 7 January 1864.

5 *WMN*, 23 August 1864.

6 *WMN*, 15 April 1872.

7 D. B. Barton, *The mines and mineral railways of East Cornwall and West Devon*, 1964.

8 C. R. Clinker, *Railway Magazine*, May 1951.

9 J. Thornton Burge, *Railway Magazine*, 1898.

10 C. Noall, *Cornish Mail and stage coaches*, 1963. The service continued until about 1908.

11 *WDM*, 17 November 1882.

12 Kelly's *Directory*, 1893.

CHAPTER TEN

1 *PDWJ*, 25 February 1858.
2 *PDWJ*, 24 April 1851.
3 *PDWJ*, 9 January 1851.
4 The figures are an estimate given by the late R. W. Toll who was closely associated with the reopening of this mine.

CHAPTER ELEVEN

Details of the building of the London & South Western Railway line between Lydford and Plymouth have been drawn largely from the *WMN*, 30 May 1890, which can be consulted in the local history section of the Plymouth Central Library. For the Bere Alston–Callington branch I have drawn freely on an article by Mr C. R. Clinker in the *Railway Magazine*, May 1951, and on another in July 1951 by Mr R. E. G. Read. Details of the legal squabble following the building of the viaduct are to be found in documents in the archivist's department of the Plymouth Central Library. Much assistance also came from Mr Eric Jones of the Public Relations Department, British Railways (Western Region), the station staff at Bere Alston and Callington, and from Mr F. Quant of Tavistock, a retired South Western Railway enthusiast who placed much of his material, the result of many years' research, at my disposal.

1 *WDM*, 16 January 1888.
2 Except at Harford Bridge, Peter Tavy, where 'hard blue rock very useful for bridge building' had to be blasted for a cutting 30 ft deep.
3 It reaches its highest point just opposite the junction of the Walkham and Tavy rivers.
4 The work was done by a Horrabridge mason, Mr J. Bailey.
5 There were no special opening celebrations. The Earl of Mount Edge-cumbe was presented with a little 'blue book of the railway bound in Japanese style with blue silk and containing thirty-two little "cyanotype" photographs of views from the stations, viaducts and bridges'.
6 *WMN*, 3 June 1890.
7 'South Western v Great Western: Railway Competition in Devon and Cornwall' by Jack Simmons, *Journal of Transport History*, May 1959.
8 Figures and records from an old London & South Western Railway despatch book, kindly supplied by Mr F. Quant of Tavistock.
9 *Railway Magazine*, January–June 1898.
10 Lang's separate estimates for the three parts of the line were: Bere Alston section (1 mile 42 chains) £9,970; viaduct (286 yards) £31,979 12s 6d;

Cornwall section (2 miles 42 chains) £12,930 16s 9d.
11 Venning's *Map and Historical Notices of East Cornwall*, Parts I–IV, 1934.
Venning's estimate of the total cost appears in the *WDM*, 9 October 1909.
The authorized capital for the line's construction, according to the *Railway Magazine*, 1908, was £145,000.
12 The third engine, *A. S. Harris*, left the branch soon after the outbreak of the last war and was used in the London area.

CHAPTER TWELVE

The general picture of agriculture in the Tamar Valley has been built up from the following authorities: R. Fraser, *General View of the Agriculture of Cornwall*, 1794 (and his companion volume on Devon); William Marshall, *The Rural Economy of the West of England*, 1796; G. B. Worgan, *General View of the Agriculture of Cornwall*, 1808; W. F. Karkeek, *On the Farming of Cornwall*, 1843; J. Allen, *History of Liskeard*, 1856; A. Voelcker, *The use of Lime, Marl and Shell Sand in Agriculture*, 1859; and the *Victoria County History of Cornwall* (the Devon *Victoria* scarcely mentions the Tamar Valley). Of these, Worgan and Karkeek are the most useful, the latter being particularly valuable in comparing the progress made from Worgan's day.

For modern times an indispensable paper is Katherine H. Johnstone's 'Horticulture in the Tamar Valley' (reprinted from *Agriculture*, 1955) which has been freely drawn on for this account. A useful study was also made by D. J. Goodchild, former district horticultural officer in East Cornwall for the National Agricultural Advisory Service. Thanks are also due to Ald F. Rogers, of St Dominic, whose firm pioneered the heat treatment of bulbs in the Tamar Valley and Mr S. Richards, of Cargreen, who gave up an evening to talk about fruit growing and market gardening in Landulph and Cargreen.
1 The dufflin cider apple was propagated experimentally at Long Ashton Research Station, Bristol, between 1903 and 1918 and distributed in a number of trial orchards in the West Country. A few of these trees still remain—one at the research station. It is an early-flowering, sharp variety, believed to have originated in Cornwall, with soft fruit which rots rapidly on falling; today the demand is for bitter-sweet cider apples. Dr L. F. Burroughs of the Cider & Fruit Juices section, Long Ashton, says the dufflin apple usually produces 'a medium bodied cider of average to good quality. It is, however, too acid to be properly compared with the heavier, low acid bittersweet ciders typical of south Somerset'. Cider, despite Lysons's comment, was never made in the Tamar Valley on the scale found in the South Hams, although the brews from one or two farm-houses at Bere Alston and Stoke Climsland gained a notoriety beyond their immediate neighbourhood.

PART TWO

Gazetteer

THE most extensive fingerprints of the Tamar Valley's industrial past are hidden underground in the miles of flooded and silent levels and cavities. On the surface the scrap metal drives demanded by two world wars have taken away much of interest. Until shortly before the last war it was still possible to find remains of water-wheels on Devon Friendship and Devon Great Consols mines; on the latter, until 1939 the arsenic flues and furnaces built after the mine closed in 1903 were still intact, even to the arsenic casks which had been assembled ready for filling and were abandoned when arsenic working on the mine finally came to an end in about 1930. Almost all this has now disappeared. The picturesque old engine house at Wheal Betsy, above Mary Tavy, well over a hundred years old, narrowly escaped destruction early in 1950 because it was alleged to be unsafe; its future preservation is by no means sure. Wind and weather are slowly disintegrating the engine house of West Wheal Crebor, at Gulworthy, almost the only substantial reminder on the surface of the old Crebor mine.

All this points to an immediate need for an exhaustive survey that will plot mines, shafts, mills, brick and tile works, tramways and major leat courses before time, developments and 'improvements' obliterate them. The present book has attempted to survey some of the valley's more important industries and features and to relate them in historical perspective. Much still remains to be told and even more to be found out. A complete survey calls for the devoted skill and labour over many years of a dozen or more enthusiasts. It is particularly urgently needed in the Gunnislake area where a uniquely dense complex of industries such as mining,

256 The Tamar Valley

manufacturing, smelting and quarrying were closely intermingled. To some extent the groundwork for such a survey is provided by the 6-in maps of the neighbourhood, and the 25-in maps of the 1880 survey, in particular, provide valuable evidence of much that is lost or in ruins today.

The list of buildings and features outlined below makes no claim to be exhaustive, but it is hoped that it will serve as a guide to much that is historically interesting and not always easily found. The text carries extended reference to many of the places and areas mentioned, but here they have been grouped under parishes for easier reference.

DEVON

BERE ALSTON AND BERE FERRERS

Tamar smelting works. Adjoining Weir Quay. Probably erected in the early 1820s. The dwelling house now facing the road was once the offices. Behind the large entrance gates, the original paved yard and some of the ore-storage sheds can still be seen, but furnaces and retort buildings which formed two sides of a square have been demolished, leaving traces of some of the furnace arches. The huge stack which carried the 'mephitic vapours' above the Valley was felled towards the end of the last century.

Union smelting house. This, about 100 yd above to the north, is much better preserved. It dates probably from the 1830s. The dwelling houses on either side were the assay office and the count house.

Johnson's Square. Although not now thus named, this is the group of houses just outside Bere Alston on the road to Hole's Hole. Johnson built it for his workpeople in the 1840s. The large rectangular building, roughly 50 × 30 ft, was the school, provided at the same time. It originally had two windows on its front wall, but one has been replaced by a sliding door.

Weir Quay. Opposite the Tamar smelting works, from where silver was shipped and coal and ores for smelting unloaded from many parts of the world. It is still in relatively good condition.

The remaining traces of the mines have been described in Chapter Three. Dotted among them can be seen forlorn clumps of cherry trees, remnants of the orchards that once swept almost unbroken down the length of the peninsula. The road running along by Hole's Hole and Weir Quay is one of the best vantage points from which to appreciate the majestic estuary of the Tamar. Besides a great wealth of bird life, there is a salt-marsh flora here of outstanding interest containing over sixty different species of plants as well as one of the smallest grasshoppers in the kingdom.

GULWORTHY

The crossroads by the church (originally built by the Duke of Bedford for the Morwellham and Gulworthy mining community) offers the best approach to Devon Great Consols mine. The road to Chipshop (which is signposted) marked the farthest point east (although this was not realized at the time) to which the great main lode extended. A little way along on the left is Honey Tor farm where the old 'dry' (miners' changing house) at Wheal Emma still exists. Close to it a clump of trees marks the site of the Eastern shaft from where the abortive mile-long level to Mill Hill was started. The incline connecting Wheal Emma to the mine railway can be traced as well as the reservoir supplying condensing water to the incline shaft engine. Near the bottom of the incline is a stone marking the site of Railway shaft (260 fathoms) where the last serious exploration on the mine for tin was carried out.

Wheal Josiah. Farther along the same road and signposted. The Hare & Hounds public house nearby has a collection of nineteenth-century mining tokens, some of them showing one of the wheels of Devon Friendship mine. The row of cottages on the road to the mine site was originally the stables for horses carting ore to Morwellham. Some of the most extensive traces of arsenic burning on Devon Great Consols are here: flues, calcining houses and condensing chambers can be seen. The grinding house has its mill stone *in situ* and close by is the pit of the water-wheel working it. The ground abounds in mineral specimens—pyrites, malachite, azurite, mundic chips, and a red gash indicating ochre. Farther to the west is Wheal Maria where the mine originally started.

HURDWICK FARM

On the Bren Tor road, contains the famous Hurdwick quarries from which most of the better buildings in Tavistock, including the church, are built. The stone is a form of lava with a warm green hue. The quarries are disused.

LUMBURN FOUNDRY AND MILL

At Lumburn Corner, on the main Tavistock–Gunnislake road. The group of buildings facing the cottages across the valley were an iron and brass foundry where, until the first world war, agricultural tools for local use were made and repaired. More interesting as a building is the old corn mill opposite; until 1964, when it was damaged by fire, the water-wheel with its corn-grinding machinery was intact. The wooden partition enclosing the wheel contained a series of chutes through which different grades of meal were delivered after being milled.

MARY TAVY, PETER TAVY AND HORNDON

All three grew up around the Devon Friendship mine, whose extensive remains form a considerable part of Mary Tavy parish.

The 60-ton barge, probably built by May of Calstock about 1870 seen off Bull Point, near Plymouth, in the 1920s. The high peaked mainsail with point reefing and a staysail was typical of the rigging of this type of barge which plied mainly between the Tamar quays and Plymouth. Similar craft were the Lynher, Elizabeth *and* Flora May, *all built at Calstock. Some of them lasted on the river until the 1930s*

Cotehele Quay about 1900 with a Tamar paddle steamer—probably the Empress— *alongside*

Calstock quay in 1894

Weir Head about 1880. The lockgates of the Tamar Manure canal can be seen in the middle of the picture with a barge tied up inside the canal. The chimneys in the middle background are probably the Bealeswood brickworks

Some of this mine's features have been noted in Chapter Seven. The early Georgian residence on the mine site with its projecting upper-storey window was the mine captain's house, and from the window 'pitches' were auctioned to tributers standing below. Horndon, which grew up as a settlement to house Devon Friendship miners, still has a few of the old stone cottages built in John Taylor's day, and an idea of their original interior can be gained from the parlour of the nearby inn. The little byroad to Horndon runs near Wheal Jewell and the Duchy United mines, which produced tin and arsenic. Cows in this neighbourhood still sometimes sicken from arsenic poisoning after spoil heaps have been disturbed by gales, and children are cautioned about picking blackberries which grow near the dumps.

Above Mary Tavy on the left-hand side of the road to Oke-hampton and almost opposite Wheal Betsy's engine house is Gibbett Hill, where there are traces of shafts and other workings for tin.

MILL HILL

Chiefly interesting for its slate quarry which has a history of almost 400 years of intermittent working and once supplied slate to the Channel Islands. The course of the 'cut' built from Taylor's canal to serve this quarry is described in Chapter Six.

MORWELLHAM

The road at the top of the hill to Morwellham divides, one branch going off and signposted to Newquay. On the road down to Mor-wellham the southern portal of the Tavistock Canal tunnel should be noted, as well as the remainder of the canal (now dry) as it swings round the hillside to the head of the original incline. Here the outlines of the old canal basin are preserved and in the contem-porary cottage above it lived the canal keeper. The path of Taylor's

Q

incline to Morwellham quay is no longer discernible, but at the foot
an old water-wheel once used to help drive the manganese mill and
later to pump water for the village is *in situ*. Traces of the old
incline rails can be found. Devon Great Consols incline a few yards
from it remains visible in parts.

Other features at Morwellham have been noted in Chapter Two.
It is still possible to walk from Morwellham to Newquay by the
river—a well-trodden path in the days of Morwellham's prosperity
—and it was along here the railway projected in 1876 was to run, to
link Morwellham with the East Cornwall Mineral Railway. The
Duke of Bedford's old riverside drive from Morwellham to Endsleigh over which Queen Victoria rode in 1856 is easily traceable for
much of the way through into Blanchdown plantation. The adjoining quays of Newquay and Gawton offer fertile ground for detailed
investigation. The large area cleared at Newquay to take the overflow of copper ore from Devon Great Consols mine in the late 1840s
can be made out, and ruined houses and sheds bear mute evidence
of what was once a busy little community with its own inn. By the
roadside at Rock a direction stone still has chiselled on it 'to Gawton
Quay'; if this is followed in conjunction with plainly marked sign-
posts farther along, the old track into Gawton mine and its adjoining
quay can fairly easily be picked up. The ruins of the old arsenic-
reduction works (where Gawton prided itself on making the 'best
arsenic in the Tamar Valley') are the most prominent feature, along
with ruined storehouses, on the quay. The engine house on the
hillside marks Bayly's shaft. At the back of it the large reservoir
which supplied water for the engines is virtually intact.

TAVISTOCK

Foundries. Outstanding is the complex of buildings in Parkham
Road which made up Rundle's and Gill's foundry or the 'Tavistock
engine works', as the faded painted sign on the foundry wall pro-

claims. The main foundry is rough, heavy and functional in appearance, but the smaller buildings adjoining are less so, and typical of nineteenth-century workshop design. In recent years part of this foundry was used as a wool-combing mill and when this ceased working in 1965 it marked the end of an industry with which Tavistock has been associated since medieval times. Some, if not all of this group of buildings, are worth preserving.

In Bannawell Street, just below Tavistock North station, stands the old foundry building of Nicholls, Williams & Co, through whose doors came many of the pumping engines for the neighbouring mines. Now used by a motor-hire firm, its boldly arched windows and characteristic nineteenth-century design lend it a modest dignity.

A third, or Tavy Foundry, is in Dolvin Road, adjoining a garage, but has little architectural interest. In the cemetery next to it is a headstone raised by public subscription to mark the grave of three miners drowned in July 1880 when they accidentally holed in the Tavy and flooded East Crebor mine.

Tavistock Canal. The 2-mile towpath walk from Tavistock to the canal's northern portal is one of the most beautiful in the district. The path leads past the site of Wheal Crowndale, where a timbered shaft adjoins the spoil heap marking some work done on the mine in the 1920s. About 20 yd from the tunnel's mouth is the entrance to the incline shaft into Wheal Crebor. The canal basin at Tavistock still retains an early nineteenth-century atmosphere with Georgian cottages and buildings formerly used as storehouses to serve the canal. On the west of the present car park was the ore yard, where lead and copper from Wheal Betsy and Wheal Friendship were dumped before being carried over the canal to Morwellham for shipment down the Tamar.

Fitzford Church. A little-regarded relic of Tavistock's mining prosperity, but worth a glance because of its curiously Italianate interior more suited to the plains of Lombardy than the banks of the

Tamar. It was put up by the Duke of Bedford in 1865–7 to cater for the overflow mining population. Built in the Lombardo-Venetian style, with a detached bell tower, its architect was Henry Clutton, who was received into the Roman church. Fitzford church fell into disuse with the decline in mining in the district and was acquired after the last war by the district's Roman Catholic community.

Walreddon Manor Mill. This is on the road branching off from Tavistock cemetery and was part of Walreddon manor which once belonged to the Courtenay family. It still retains its water-wheel and grinding machinery. On the left, at the top of the hill farther along the same road, are the shafts and dumps of Rix Hill, or Anderton mine, which probably still contains tin and whose main shaft comes up in a farmyard. Opposite, in Birch Tor plantation, overlooking the Tavy, was the Devon & Courtenay mine, which produced copper in small amounts and was served by an overhead cable railway.

Westbridge and Fitzford Cottages. These are worth noting as examples of mid-nineteenth-century industrial housing whose design and layout remain pleasing. Opposite West Bridge cottages and behind the now-disused gasworks was Wheal Crelake mine, whose dump can still be seen and whose levels ran under the Tavy.

CORNWALL

CALSTOCK

There is more to see on the road approaching Calstock than in the town itself. One of the most vivid and arresting mine panoramas in the district unfolds as one approaches Calstock church from Gunnislake. The workings of Wheal Edward and Wheal Arthur are on the left, and to the right is the ruined engine house of Calstock Consols. Ahead looms the stack of long-disused Wheal Zion, while the sprawling dumps of Drakewalls form a mining background to the north. In this stretch of countryside the old East Cornwall Mineral Railway started life. Its cutting, passing under the road to the head of the incline, is easy to discern, forming with the disused water tower and old wagon-repair shed a photogenic cluster of past industrial history. In Calstock itself chief interest lies along the river front, where the outlines of the old quays are fairly well preserved. That by the Danescombe Hotel (built in 1859 as the Ashburton hotel to cater for the river traffic) was the principal quay from which granite was shipped. At the other end part of the old copper quay has been adapted as a recreation ground, although kerbing which marked the course of the horse-drawn tramway along the quay can still be seen. Above the quays the track of the old incline is visible, winding round the shoulder of the hill. Where the wagons debouched on to the quay is the little brick building now shuttered and empty where the horses took over.

The factory-like building with the squat stack seen on descending the hill into Calstock which now serves as a chip-basket factory was one of Westlake's brick works.

Calstock Church. Worth visiting for the quaintly carved slate tombstones in its churchyard, many of them recalling fatal accidents in the neighbouring mines. Calstock itself remains yet to be 'discovered'.

GUNNISLAKE

Along with Chilsworthy, preserves more vividly than Tavistock the atmosphere of the mining and quarrying industries around which it grew. There are many examples of early industrial cottage housing in Gunnislake, particularly near the bottom of Newbridge Hill and again facing Pearson's quarry above the town centre.

Clitter's mine. Sprawls over a thickly wooded hillside north of the town, and has traces of the tramroad near the river bank which served the mine until the East Cornwall Mineral line was built.

More difficult to pick up without a map is the track of the incline plane leading from the arsenic works on the river bank to Skinner's shaft and linking the mine to the railway.

Brick and tile works. There are substantial traces of this industry, which was carried on until the 1930s. Best preserved are the brick kilns adjoining the Greenhill arsenic works. Brick and tile making was also carried on extensively at the Plymouth firebrick works to the east of Greenhill, where the chief feature was a large circular kiln connected by a tramway to the adjoining clay pit. A spur line from the railway also served these works, which, like the Sandhill brickworks whose remains lie below, have been disused for over fifty years.

Greenhill arsenic works. Smelting as well as arsenic burning was carried on here, the complex of buildings and ruins stretching both sides of the Chilsworthy–Gunnislake road. The two halves were joined by an incline plane, and a siding connected them to the railway. The works closed in 1925. Arsenic produced here was sent among other places to Piraeus (Greece) and South America for insecticides and sheep dips. An exceptionally pure form made up for the British drug industry was used by them as a standard.

The river bank at Gunnislake is also worth attention. The passage of over seventy years has obliterated traces of the short tramway which connected the old Bealeswood brickworks to its claypit although part of the works' engine house still remains. Along the towpath from these works to Gunnislake Bridge are the crumbling remains of a smithy which once served Gunnislake Old mine, some of whose shafts are on the hillside above it, and the spoil heaps of Snowden's quarry, which produced granite setts to pave Plymouth's streets. The stone was trammed to the river bank for loading into barges. Farther down the river towards Whimple was Netstakes quay, now grass-covered, where Emanuel Crocker launched the *Tamar Queen,* and close by are the crumbling walls of the old Tamar bone and fertilizer works.

HARROWBARROW

Coombe arsenic works. These were active in the 1920s treating arsenic not only from a number of mines in the neighbourhood but from Devon Great Consols in its later reworking. Development threatens these ruins, which include the outlines of an intricate pattern of ovens and flues.

KIT HILL

The extensive granite quarry workings are on the south side. Although not now worked they retain the incline plane which connected them to the railway below. Its 3 ft 6 in gauge is that of the old Mineral railway. The Excelsior tunnel begins in a wood in the bottom of the valley north of Kithill about 800 yd north-north-west of Monks Cross.

LUCKETT

Probably preserves a better picture of past mining activity than any other place in the Tamar Valley. Prominent in its valley is the ruined steam whim house of Wheal Martha around which Luckett is built. Its hauling engine was *in situ* until removed for scrap in the last war. Wheal Martha was first a tin producer but in the early 1870s turned over to arsenic production in an ambitious way, and a line of stacks marks the course of a mile-long length of flues stretching south towards Kit Hill to end in a solitary stack still standing in a field below Monk's Corner. The flues leaked so badly that the village school which adjoins them had to close for a time, vegetation in the valley was poisoned (or so it was claimed), and an injunction was sought against the company.

Prominent on a bank above the steam whim house is the old

north engine house; from a shaft directly in front of it the mine was opened up in 1947 for wolfram and tin. A long dump extending into a field marks the site of this reworking, which was connected by a now-dismantled overhead cableway to a crushing mill higher up the valley. Around Luckett are the ruins and workings of Wheal Sheba, Wheal Benny, Wheal Duchy and Wheal Tom, combining to make the village of unique importance for the industrial archaeologist. It remains today an astonishing outpost of industrial enterprise in a remote countryside.

ST ANN'S CHAPEL

Contains typical miners' cottages and is probably the best place from which to approach the old fireclay workings immediately above it on Hingston Down. Here were the Phoenix Brickworks, which exported to Russia, the Calstock Firebrick Works and the extensive Tamar Firebrick Works, described in Chapter Two.

CARGREEN

This is a typical Tamar 'passage' point, touched by mining to the north where at Wheal Hancock or the Park mine one of the most southerly extensions of the Bere Alston lead lodes were worked in a small way.

MODITANHAM

Below Cargreen, once famous for its fruit and has a pleasant Georgian house, once the home of Michael Loam, who patented the first practical Cornish man engine and who was the engineer for a number of mines in the neighbourhood.

HORTICULTURE

Although fruit and flowers are extensively grown around Bere Alston, the area from Calstock southward to Cargreen provides the best evidence of past and present fruit and flower growing. Here are the fruitful Danescombe and Bohetherick Valleys, Burcombe where the cherries of that name originated, and St Mellion, St Dominic, Botus Fleming and Halton Quay. It is a land golden with daffodils in the spring and rich with the smell of fruit in the summer. Botus Fleming, which boasted five public houses (it has one today) when the Tamar was full of barges, has hundred-year-old cherry trees still bearing fruit, although no longer can one buy the fiercely named but sweet eating Green Stem Rumbullion. The area between Botus Fleming and Halton quay is one of the few in the Tamar Valley where cherries are now grown in any quantity.

Bibliographical Notes

THE following abbreviations are used:

DCNQ   *Devon & Cornwall Notes & Queries*
DCRO   *Devon County Record Office*
PDWJ   *Plymouth & Devonport Weekly Journal*
TDA   *Transactions* of the Devonshire Association
TPI   *Transactions* of the Plymouth Institution
WB   *West Briton*
WDM   *The Western Daily Mercury*
WMN   *The Western Morning News*

No book has hitherto examined the Tamar Valley as a whole and therefore the picture built up in the foregoing pages has had to be drawn from many sources. Much information from 1850 onwards has come from the files of the now-extinct *Plymouth & Devonport Weekly Journal* and *Plymouth Mail*, and from *The Western Morning News* and the newspaper it absorbed, *The Western Daily Mercury*. The files can be consulted in the local history department of the Plymouth Central Library. A considerable mass of material relating to the Devon side of the Valley is still to be sifted from the Bedford Estate papers, now deposited at the Devon County Record Office, Exeter, and only recently generally available. Much information has also been derived from talking with people in the Valley. Generally, books and sources mentioned in the text and notes have not been repeated in the following list.

GENERAL HISTORIES, STUDIES AND
REMINISCENCES

DEVON

Among the histories, Polwhele's *Devonshire* (1793–1806), has occasional value. Much more useful is Risdon's *Survey of the County of Devon* (1811), particularly the highly characteristic introduction by John Taylor. Lysons's *Magna Britannica*, Vol. 6, (1822), is informative and interesting about early industries and has particularly useful notes (supplied by John Taylor) on early mining ventures. Moore's *History of Devonshire*, 1829–36, is incomplete like most histories of Devon, but supplements a good deal of Lysons's information. Moore is the sole source of much early information about the Tamar manure canal. R. N. Worth's separate histories of Devonport and Plymouth, 1870–2, L. Jewitt's *History of Plymouth*, 1873, and H. F. Whitfield's *Plymouth and Devonport in War and Peace*, 1900, help to fill out the general nineteenth-century picture. Frank Vosper's *Rural Life Sketches*, 1870, written after the author had gone to live in British Columbia, offer a good picture of life and incidents in the Tamar Valley from the middle of the last century. Indispensable modern works are H. P. R. Finberg's *Tavistock Abbey*, 1951, especially useful on early agricultural practice, and W. G. Hoskins's *Devon*, 1954, which is not only stimulating in approach but is a most valuable source book. Invaluable also are Finberg and Hoskins's *Devonshire Studies*, 1952. Mrs A. E. Bray's *The Borders of the Tamar and Tavy*, first published 1838, and Rachel Evans's *Home Scenes; or Tavistock and its Vicinity*, 1846, give vivid pictures of the Devon side of the valley in the early nineteenth century and should be read in conjunction with Mrs Rundle Charles's *Our Seven Homes*. For suggestions and theories on early tracks and roads, Hencken's *The Archaeology of Cornwall and the Scilly Isles*, 1932, is valuable. J. L. W. Page's *The Rivers of Devon*, 1893, discusses the Tamar and Tavy pleasantly, and Arthur H. Norway's *Highways and Byways in Devon*, 1897, although over-ornamental in style is richly enthusiastic about the scenery of the Tamar. Highly characteristic and still eminently readable is Rev S. Baring-Gould's *Book of the South-west*, Vol. 11, 1899, which has an interesting chapter on arsenic burning. Generally Baring-Gould's Westcountry books are full of sidelights on the customs and history of the area, as for example Lew Trenchard church being built of unmortared limestone brought from Plymouth, while lime cement from the stone quarried near Lifton was used for external pointing and internal plastering in the church.

CORNWALL

Carew's *Survey*, 1602, and Borlase's *Natural History*, 1758, allowing for the period in which they were written, are treasure houses. Most of the other histories up to the middle of the nineteenth century are too cluttered with genealogies and guesses about Druids, Phoenecians and Romans to be of great value, although Fortescue Hitchens's *History of Cornwall*, 1824, and Davies Gilbert's *Parochial History*, 1838, supply information of value. The latter has some useful summaries and quaint but not valueless notes on the geology of areas like Calstock. Bond's *Histories of East and West Looe*, 1826, and Allen's *History of Liskeard*, 1856, have considerable background value, and so have the two histories of Launceston by R. and O. B. Peter, 1885, and A. F. Robbins, 1888. In 1843 Cyrus Redding published an *Illustrated Itinerary of Cornwall*, which recalls an excursion up the Tamar and has some valuable population statistics. Alfred Pengelly's *The Inside story of Calstock*, a booklet published in 1955 but now difficult to find, is one of the few records of life and industry around Calstock towards the end of the last century. Of the two *Victoria County Histories*, the volume for *Devon* has little to say about the Tamar Valley; that for *Cornwall* is much more valuable, containing perceptive chapters on the scenery and granite working and some useful information on the market-gardening industry. The *Cornwall Survey*, published in 1930 in collaboration with the CPRE, is illuminating on the Tamar's tributaries, while Henderson's *Old Cornish Bridges and Streams*, 1928, contains much of incidental interest. An excellent and invaluable source book for mining and agricultural information is Dr J. Rowe's *Cornwall and the Industrial Revolution*, 1948.

TOPOGRAPHICAL WORKS, TOURS, &c

Most of these relate to Cornwall, and the best, mainly produced in the late eighteenth and early nineteenth centuries, are alive with piquant details which although not specifically related to the Tamar Valley are sufficiently generalized to present an authentic picture of the district. Among those consulted have been: *The Tours of Celia Fiennes 1685–1705* (she caught a bad cold from getting a wetting on one of the Tamar ferries); *The Travels through England of Bishop Pockocke*, 1750, which contains a reference to early pottery manufacture at Calstock; Stebbing Shaw's *A Tour through the West of England*, 1798; Rev William Gilpin's *Observations on the Western parts of England*, 1798; Dr W. G. Maton's *Observations on the Western Counties of England, 1794–96*; Rev Richard Warner's *A Tour through Cornwall in the Autumn of 1808*; F. W. L. Stockdale's *A Tour Through Cornwall*, 1824. Stockdale notes the cruelty often attending the use of packhorses. Particularly illuminating for its theories and explanations on early settlement and field boundaries in East Cornwall and on the west bank of the Tamar is N. V. Balchin's *The Geography of Cornwall*, 1954.

PERIODICALS

Among those consulted have been *The Western Antiquary,
Devonia, Devon & Cornwall Notes & Gleanings* (and its successor
Devon & Cornwall Notes & Queries), the *Transactions* of the Devonshire Association and the *Transactions* of the Plymouth Institution.
The two latter are particularly valuable, but all these yield information either in notes or articles from the early part of the last century
down to the present day. Since this book was finished some interesting information about shipping on the Tamar has come to light from
documents and papers found in an old property at Saltash, and is
being reproduced in current editions of *DCNQ*.

GAZETTEERS AND DIRECTORIES

These often prove the best sources of factual information. One of
the first of value was White's *History, Gazetteer and Directory of
Devonshire*, 1850, which records the now-vanished inns and trades
on many of the quays on the Devon bank of the Tamar. A second
edition (1878) has valuable references to the mines then working.
The last edition (1890) is a mass of interesting and often extremely
readable information. White's work is to some extent supplemented
by Kelly's *Directories*, of which those for Devon and Cornwall first
appeared in 1856 and continued at intervals until 1939. They make
possible the building up of, for instance, a vivid picture of the
industrial rise and decline of Calstock. Murray's *Handbook for
Devon and Cornwall* (first published 1850 but two subsequent
editions for Devon alone appeared in 1879 and 1895), besides giving
useful facts shows how highly regarded the area was as a beauty spot,
a theme embellished by a continuous succession of guide books

published from Plymouth and Devonport from the beginning of the 1800s until 1914. Those by Rowe, Carrington and Hearder are particularly worth consulting and can occasionally be picked up at sales. All of these last can be found in the Plymouth Central Library's local history department.

GEOLOGY AND MINING

Sir Henry de la Bèche's *Report on the geology of Cornwall, Devon and West Somerset*, 1839, is a *locus classicus* and despite being over a hundred years old is still one of the best introductions to geology and mining in the area. The 1911 *Geological Survey Memoirs* of the Tavistock–Launceston and Plymouth–Liskeard districts have a slight period flavour and that for Tavistock–Launceston is ill-arranged and poorly written. Nevertheless both are indispensable for any study of the area and contain valuable mining-output tables and bibliographies. The Plymouth volume has a notable tribute to the work of R. N. Worth. More up-to-date assessments are those of H. Dewey in his *British Regional Geology: South West England*, second edition 1948, and G. M. Barton's *The Geology of Cornwall*, 1966. The Tavistock area, however, is overdue for an up-to-date geological survey and assessment. A good history and survey is also needed of the Plymouth limestone deposits. A. W. Clayden's *The history of Devonshire Scenery*, 1906, is most useful in helping towards an understanding of physical features and should be read along with W. H. Thompson's and G. C. Clark's *The Devon Landscape*, 1934.

There is an extensive literature about metalliferous mining in Devon and Cornwall, but little is directly concerned with the Tamar Valley. Essential background works are the *Transactions* of the Royal Cornwall Polytechnic Society and the Royal Cornwall Geological Society. H. L. Dines's *The Metalliferous Mining Region of the South West of England*, Vol. II, 1956, describes in close detail the mine workings in the area and has useful summaries of outputs and geological indications. D. M. Barton's *Copper Mining in Cornwall*, 1958, and *Historical Survey of the Mines and Mineral Railways of East Cornwall and South West Devon*, 1964, have skilful and useful summaries of the historical background of most of the mines of the area, and the same author's *The Cornish Beam Engine*, 1966, besides being a standard work on its subject has references to the foundries in the district. An older book, but in its way never likely to be superseded, is J. H. Collins's *Observations on the West of England Mining Region*, 1912. It is difficult to obtain outside a library, but valuable because Collins not only had detailed knowledge but a close connection with almost all the leading mines in the area. He also edited, and indeed virtually wrote, the *Proceedings* of The London & Westcountry Chamber of Mines, issued at intervals over a number of years from the beginning of the century, a storehouse of useful information on the output and working of many local mines. J. Darlington and J. H. Phillips's *Records of Mining and Metallurgy*, 1857, gives details about the lodes of Devon Great Consols mine, while Andrée's *A Treatise on Mining Machinery* has fascinating information and sectional drawings of some of the water-wheels of this mine. For the general picture of the metal miner's life in the area nothing better has been published than A. K. Hamilton Jenkin's *The Cornish Miner*, third edition, 1962. Much other interesting information about mining in the area in the early and middle years of the nineteenth century can be found in John Taylor's *Records of Mining*, 1829, T. Y. Watson's *A Compendium of British Mining*, reissued 1964, Williams's *Cornwall and Devon Mining Directory*, 1860, and Thomas Spargo's *The Mines of Cornwall*, 1865 (reissued). More about lead and silver mining can be found in articles by J. Carne, 'On the Discovery of Silver in the Mines of Cornwall', *Transactions* of the Royal Geological Society of Cornwall, Vol. I, 1818; W. J. Henwood, *Transactions* of the Royal Geological Society of Cornwall, Vol. VIII, Part 1, 1871; and

Collins, 'The Precious Metals of the West of England', *Journal* of the Royal Institution of Cornwall, Vol. XVI, 1904; and in Vol. XXI of the *Memoirs of the Geological Survey*, 1921, which deals with the lead, silver-lead and zinc ores of Cornwall, Devon and Somerset. Webb and Geach's *The history and progress of mining in the Caradon and Liskeard district*, second edition, 1863, which can be consulted in the reference libraries of Plymouth and Redruth, has interesting material about a region immediately bordering the Tamar Valley. Pryce's *Mineralogia Cornubiensis*, 1778, although a fascinating pioneer work, is largely of antiquarian interest. On the granite industry, G. F. Harris's *Granites and our granite industries*, 1888, is not without interest.

AGRICULTURE

Apart from the surveys of Worgan and Karkeet, mentioned in the notes, two of the best sources for forming a picture of late eighteenth- and early nineteenth-century agricultural progress in the area are William Marshall's *The Rural economy of the West of England*, 1796, and C. Vancouver's *General View of the Agriculture of Devon*, 1808. Marshall ranges widely from fish traps to limekilns, is illuminating on liming techniques and about the state of ditches and roads, and his comments are acute, occasionally caustic. Vancouver supplements him and adds, incidentally, some detailed information about the Tavistock Canal. The notes (by his son) to N. T. Carrington's poem *Dartmoor* have details about cultivation on Dartmoor in the region of Princetown.

COMMUNICATIONS

For dates and general details, E. T. MacDermot's *History of the Great Western Railway*, 1927 (revised and republished 1964) and

R

C. F. Dendy Marshall's *A History of the Southern Railway*, 1936, are essential. C. Hamilton Ellis's *The South Western Railway*, 1956, is useful for details of locomotives and rolling stock. For the general background to railway history in the district D. St J. Thomas's volume on the Westcountry (third edition, 1966) in the *Regional History of the Railways of Great Britain* series is a valuable guide. For canals, Charles Hadfield's *The Canals of Southern England*, 1955, is informative and accurate, while useful information about early stage-coach services is in C. Noall's *A History of Cornish Mail and Stage Coaches*, 1963. There is no published material about the Tamar steamers. C. Henderson's *Essays in Cornish History*, 1935, has facts about the early history of some Tamar ferries.

RECENT WORKS

The surveys of Devon and Cornwall carried out since the last war bring together up-to-date information, some of which is relevant to the Tamar Valley. Two recent manuscript sources which can be consulted in the Plymouth City Library's local history section are a survey of the Tamar Valley by Phyllis Tate, which is a perceptive study of the area, mainly from physical aspects, and Owen A. Baker's pioneer study on the geology and mines of the area, which gained for its author the Bolitho silver medal of the Royal Cornwall Geological Society. A dissertation by A. M. Wherry on the influence of mining and landownership in the Tavistock neighbourhood is thought-provoking and contains some useful mineral production diagrams.

Acknowledgements

I HAVE received much help in writing this book. Some has been acknowledged in the text and notes, but there are many other people to whom I am indebted. I would particularly like to mention Mr P. Kennedy, the Devon County and Diocesan Archivist and his staff at the Devon County Record Office, Exeter, who often at very short notice searched for and obtained records for me, and have made available photostat copies of maps and plans. I also owe a deep debt to Mr W. Best Harris and the staff of the local history section of the Plymouth City Library for their kindness in searching for obscure newspaper files and for helpful suggestions. My thanks are also due to the staff of the Cornwall County Record Office at Truro, to Mr P. Hull, the Cornwall County Archivist, and to Mr K. D. Holt, the Plymouth City Archivist, who drew my attention to the records of the arbitration action following the building of the Calstock viaduct. For some useful hints on early shipping from Calstock I am indebted to Mr Richard Pearse.

The chapter and appendix on the Tamar steamers could not have been completed without the generous help of Mr Geoffrey Clark, of Plymouth, and of Miss E. Gale of the Millbrook Steamboat Company's office at Cremyll.

Mr S. Jackman of the Central Electricity Generating Board not only gave useful help on details of Taylor's canal but allowed me to accompany him on an inspection tour through the tunnel. Much help with pictures and information about leats and quarries was given me by Mr F. Warren of Gunnislake, while Messrs John Taylor & Sons kindly supplied details of Taylor's life and helped in finding some of his papers to learned societies.

On the mining side I have had the benefit of the comprehensive records of Lt-Cdr P. Richardson (RN Rtd) of Totnes, who placed at my disposal his invaluable systemized list of mines in the area and greatly helped me with plans and pictures. Grateful acknowledgements are also due to Mr S. Johns of Gunnislake, Mr J. Trounson of Redruth, Mr L. J. Trevithick of Callington, Mrs B. Toll who kindly let me see many records left by her late husband Mr R. Toll, Mrs S. Pearse and Mrs B. Emptage for typing much of the manuscript, to Mr Crispin Gill for many hints and suggestions, and above all to Mr D. St J. Thomas without whose kindly persistence this book might never have been written.

For the general picture of the Tamar Valley I have derived great help from an unpublished manuscript written and lent to me by Mr Lawrence Maker of Callington who gave me much useful advice and information. In Tavistock I have been glad to make use of the wide knowledge and kindly help of Mr Eric Kingdon. For the chapters on railways in the area I owe much to the expert knowledge of Mr C. R. Clinker, who not only made available to me a great deal of information but kindly read and corrected those particular chapters. Photographs of Calstock viaduct and of the *Garlandstone* were generously provided by Mr Michael Bouquet of Bampton.

Plates 22 and 27 are reproduced by courtesy of the Cornwall County Record Office.

Plate 37 is reproduced by courtesy of A. Oliver Hill, Plate 38 by courtesy of C. Staal, Plates 39 and 40 by courtesy of Eric Kingdon.

Apart from those otherwise mentioned all the photographs have been taken by Mr P. Brierley. The maps and plans have been drawn by Mr R. Pickard and Mr W. Bone, but numbers 5, 6 and 7 are from the *Mining Magazine.**

For the rest I must record a general but sincere acknowledgement of the help of those many people in the Tamar Valley (and some now

* Number 2 is from the Geological Survey & Museum, by permission of the controller, HM Stationery Office.

living far from it) who have replied to letters and answered questions. In the six years or so it has taken to collect the information for this book the kindness and hospitality I have received in the homes of total strangers is one of my pleasantest recollections.

Finally a constant guide and help has been my wife, who has uncomplainingly endured for many months a preoccupied husband and an overflowing clutter of files and books.

APPENDIX ONE

Mine Outputs

Mineral output of principal Tamar Valley mines 1850–1880

THESE were among the peak years of copper production in the Tamar Valley. There is no completely satisfactory record of earlier outputs (except for Devon Great Consols), although in the first half of the nineteenth century there were large returns of copper, lead and silver and tin from mines like Wheal Friendship, Wheal Crebor, Drakewalls, the Gunnislake mines and from the Bere Alston silver mines. The extracts below are from the official mineral statistics and have been taken at five-yearly intervals.

Symbols: Cu copper; As arsenic; Sn tin; Ag silver; Pb lead; Mn manganese; Fe iron; W wolfram; Pyr pyrites.

Mine	Year	Tons	Value (£s)
Wheal Arthur	1852	483 Cu ore	3,559
	1855	6 Sn ore	407
	1855	2,774 Cu ore	11,229
	1860	136 Cu ore	409
	1865	1,721 Cu ore	5,176
	1875	3 Sn ore	110
	1880	2½ Sn ore	120
	1880	3½ As	21
Wheal Bedford	1852	267 Cu ore	745
Bedford Consols	1865	Probably active but no returns	
	1875	17 Cu ore	85
	1875	211 As pyr	318
Bedford United	1850	1,426 Cu ore	9,804
	1855	2,292 Cu ore	15,751
	1855	197 As pyr	

283

Mine	Year	Tons	Value ($£s$)
Bedford United	1860	2,482 Cu ore	13,556
	1865	1,914 Cu ore	8,160
	1870	946 Cu ore	2,845
	1870	224 As pyr	140
	1875	1,018 Cu ore	4,701
	1875	136 As pyr	85
	1875	44 Fluorspar	
	1880	654 Cu ore	2,316
	1880	144 As pyr	114
South Bedford			
(See also East	1860	617 Cu ore	1,849
Gunnislake and			
South Bedford)	1870	3 Pyr	
Wheal Brothers	1875	14 As	41
	1875	$\frac{1}{2}$ Cu/Ag precip.	90
Callington	1850	516 Pb ore	
	1851	147 Cu ore	755
Kelly Bray	1855	306 Cu ore	1,500

(Then see under Kelly Bray)

Mine	Year	Tons	Value ($£s$)
Callington United	1870	(See Colquite & Callington United)	
Calstock	1860	18 Pb ore	
		(400 oz Ag)	
Calstock Consols	1860	868 Cu ore	4,277
	1860	58 Pyr	64
	1865	(Possibly active but no returns given)	
	1875	12 Cu ore	38
	1875	123 Pyr	165
New Great	1870	49 Sn ore	3,322
Consols	1870	180 As	450
	1875	$17\frac{1}{2}$ Sn ore	751
	1875	493 As	3,152

Mine	Year	Tons	Value (£s)
New Great Consols	1875	53 Cu/Ag precip.	3,118
Colquite & Callington United	1870	38 Pyr	40
Cornwall Great Consols	1880	20 Sn ore	964
Coryton	1860	100 Mn ore	300
Cotehele Consols	1880	60 As pyr	45
Wheal Crebor	1852	209 Cu ore	1,345
	1855	483 Cu ore	2,306
	1860	154 Cu ore	490
	1865	525 Cu ore	2,229
	1865	62 Pyr	39
	1870	372 Cu ore	1,284
	1870	92 Pyr	
	1875	516 Cu ore	2,261
	1875	370 As pyr	402
	1880	2,885 Cu ore	11,657
	1880	414 As pyr	376
Wheal Crelake	1860	1,243 Cu ore	7,431
	1860	30 Pb ore (308 oz Ag)	
	1860	320 Pyr	138
	1865	152 Cu ore	482
	1865	69 Pb ore (892 oz Ag)	
	1865	250 Pyr	250
	1870	677 Cu ore	1,792
	1870	1,244 As pyr	1,236
Crowndale	1860	36 Cu ore	127
	1865	Probably active but no returns	
	1870	30 As pyr	19
New Crowndale	1875	10 Cu ore	24

Mine	Year	Tons	Value (£s)
New Crowndale	1875	3¼ Sn ore	136
East Crowndale	1852	72 Sn ore	719
New Devon Consols	1870	14 Pb ore	
Devon Great Consols	1850	17,089 Cu ore	109,989
	1855	23,467 Cu ore	131,294
	1860	21,920 Cu ore	109,324
	1860	2,593 Pyr	1,224
	1865	25,309 Cu ore	127,140
	1865	836 Fe pyr	595
	1870	16,332 Cu ore	49,730
	1870	2,237 As	12,558
	1870	21 ochre	53
	1875	7,481 Cu ore	29,845
	1875	104 Pyr	73
	1875	1,212 As	10,503
	1880	10,116 Cu ore	24,930
	1880	181 As pyr	320
	1880	3,149 As	26,283
Devon & Cornwall United	1852	98 Cu ore	476
	1855	341 Cu ore	1,256
	1860	1,162 Cu ore	4,464
	1860	62 Pyr	37
	1865	2,926 Cu ore	9,920
	1865	41 Fe pyr	26
	1870	172 Cu ore	511
Great Devon & Bedford	1865	Probably active but no returns given	
Devon & Courtney	1852	70 Cu ore	570
	1855	134 Cu ore	841
	1860	167 Cu ore	598
Drakewalls	1852	219 Sn ore	

Mine	Year	Tons	Value (£s)
Drakewalls	1855	301 Sn ore	20,225
	1860	176 Sn ore	14,348
	1860	20 Cu ore	117
	1860	4 lb W	
	1865	192 Sn ore	11,285
	1865	17 crude As	13
	1870	167 Sn ore	12,647
	1875	224 Sn ore	12,311
	1875	60 As soot	60
	1880	$1\frac{1}{4}$ Sn ore	51
Duchy Great	1875	111 Cu ore	275
Consols	1875	223 Pyr	303
Wheal Edward	1855	172 Cu ore	1,468
	1860	547 Cu ore	2,228
	1865	34 Cu ore	68
Fortescue Consols	1870	$5\frac{1}{4}$ Sn ore	376
(See also West Maria & Fortescue)			
Wheal Franco	1852	224 Cu ore	1,090
	1855	487 Cu ore	1,814
	1860	319 Cu ore	1,336
Franco Consols	1870	28 Cu ore	73
	1875	15 Pyr	9
Wheal Friendship	1850	No record, although there were small returns for 1848 and 1849	
	1855	1,809 Cu ore	17,067
	1860	1,678 Cu ore	15,986
	1860	$1\frac{3}{4}$ Pb ore	
	1860	339 Pyr	136
	1865	1,960 Cu ore	13,950
	1865	$2\frac{1}{2}$ Pb ore	
	1865	463 Fe pyr	347
	1870	1,090 Cu ore	5,982

Mine	Year	Tons	Value (£s)
Wheal Friendship	1870	4 Pb ore	
	1870	470 Pyr	356
	1875	160 Cu ore	1,107
	1875	3 Pb ore	40
	1875	845 Pyr	1,108
	1875	660 As	5,340
	1880	20½ Sn ore	825
	1880	22 Cu ore	75
	1880	10 As ore	10
	1880	546 As	3,183
North Wheal Friendship	1855	96 Pb ore (862 oz Ag)	
	1865	Possibly active but no returns given	
Gawton	1860	233 Cu ore	639
	1865	Probably active but no returns given	
	1870	1,274 Cu ore	4,393
	1870	137 Pyr	127
	1875	720 Cu ore	2,560
	1875	357 As pyr	441
	1880	273 Cu ore	542
	1880	334 As pyr	392
Old Gunnislake	1865	Probably active but no returns given. See under Gunnislake Clitters for 1865, however	
	1870	8½ Sn ore ('Gunnislake')	625
Gunnislake Clitters	1860	462 Cu ore	2,925
	1865	65 Sn ore	3,136
	(This figure may refer to Old Gunnislake)		
	1865	255 Cu ore	738
	1870	938 Cu ore	4,803

Mine	Year	Tons	Value (£s)
Gunnislake	1875	1,692 Cu ore	9,333
Clitters	1880	1,979 Cu ore	10,120
East Gunnislake &	1855	780 Cu ore	1,628
South Bedford	1860	788 Cu ore	2,694
	1860	1 Sn ore	70
	1865	77 Cu ore	234
	1865	123 Fe pyr	78
	1870	34 Cu ore	82
Hawkmoor	1855	331 Cu ore	2,054
	1860	576 Cu ore	2,966
	1860	48 Pyr	19
	1865	5 Sn ore	217
	1865	108 Cu ore	415
	1875	4 Sn ore	223
Haye Valley	1865	Probably active but no returns given	
	1870	$2\frac{3}{4}$ Sn ore	163
Hingston Downs	1850	75 Cu ore	831
	1855	3,318 Cu ore	20,615
	1860	1,763 Cu ore	7,138
	1865	2,929 Cu ore	12,623
	1870	220 Cu ore	454
	1870	65 Sn ore	
	1875	3,378 Cu ore	9,392
	1880	27 Cu ore	131
	1880	$10\frac{1}{2}$ Pyr	5
	1880	$7\frac{1}{2}$ As pyr	7
Hogstor	1860	832 Mn ore	2,796
(Later see Chillaton)		This is a combined figure for Hogstor, Chillaton Manor, Sydenham and Lewtrenchard but they were not necessarily working together	

Mine	Year	Tons	Value (£s)
Holmbush	1850	761 Cu ore	4,148
	1850	200 Pb ore	
	1855	1,601 Cu ore	9,790
	1860	1,052 Cu ore	7,872
	1860	20 Pb ore	
		(147 oz Ag)	
	1880	15 Cu ore	48
	1880	4,458 As pyr	5,786
	1880	910 As	5,273
Kelly Bray	1860	1,831 Cu ore	7,840
(Previously	1860	75 Pyr	25
Callington	1865	386 Cu ore	1,480
Kelly Bray)	1870	1,628 Cu ore	4,758
Kit Hill United	1860	27½ Sn ore	2,230
	1860	19 W	
	1865	17 Sn ore	1,012
Kit Hill	1870	6½ Sn ore	462
	1870	10 W	119
South Kit Hill	1870	12 Sn ore	754
	1880	15½ Sn ore	755
Wheal Langford	1852	7½ Pb ore	
	1855	7 Pb ore	
East Wheal Maria	1865	Possibly active but no returns given	
Wheal Maria &	1865	85 Cu ore	127
Fortescue or	1870	1,388 Cu ore	5,427
Maria &	1875	798 Cu ore	3,486
Fortescue	1875	277 As	555
Great Wheal Martha	1865	Possibly active but no returns given	

Mine	Year	Tons	Value (£s)
New Wheal Martha	1865	3,005 Cu ore	6,007
	1865	509 Pyr	
		These figures may refer to Great Wheal Martha	
West Wheal Martha	1865	Probably active but no returns given. Previously Great Wheal Sheba	
Great Wheal Sheba	1865	Probably active but no returns given. Previously Great Sheba Consols	
Okel Tor	1855	151 As mundic	
	1860	646 Cu ore	1,925
	1860	263 Pyr	166
	1865	1,721 Cu ore	5,176
	1865	268 Fe pyr	164
	1870	1,170 Cu ore	2,507
	1870	219 Pyr	150
	1880	5 Cu precip.	25
	1880	691 As	6,744
Prince of Wales	1865	9 Cu ore	45
	1870	1,049 Cu ore	5,340
	1875	468 Cu ore	1,700
	1880	15 Sn ore	
Redmoor	1860	13 Sn ore	1,035
	1860	39 Pb ore	
	1865	Probably active and returns may have been included with Kelly Bray	
	1870	29 Sn ore	2,185
	1870	21 As soot	47
Wheal Russell	1852	181 Cu ore	763
	1855	584 Cu ore	2,827
	1860	$15\frac{1}{2}$ Cu ore	29

Mine	Year	Tons	Value (£s)
Wheal Russell	1865	Probably active but no returns given	
	1870	534 Cu ore	2,180
	1875	1,230 Cu ore	3,880
East Russell	1860	1,101 Cu ore	8,995
	1865	843 Cu ore	3,380
	1870	55 Sn ore	3,605
New East Russell	1865	47 Cu ore	215
Great Sheba Consols	1855	1,140 Cu ore	2,588
Silver Valley & Wheal Brothers	1852	9 Pb ore	
Sortridge Consols	1855	1,138 Cu ore	12,422
	1860	269 Cu ore	1,615
	1865	242 Cu ore	959
West Sortridge	1855	6 Sn ore	325
Tamar (& Tamar Consols)	1850	977 Pb ore	
	1855	728 Pb ore (305 oz Ag)	
	1860	781 Pb ore	
	1880	16 Pb ore (126 oz Ag)	
East Tamar Consols	1850	398 Pb ore	
	1855	25 Pb ore (408 oz Ag)	
	1860	53 Pb ore (1,080 oz Ag)	
South Tamar Consols	1850	477 Pb ore	
	1855	1,325 Pb ore (59,468 oz Ag)	
	1860	60 Pb ore (2,834 oz Ag)	

Mine	Year	Tons	Value (£s)
River Tamar	1859	Probably active but no returns given	
	1870	Small amount Sn ore	17
Tamar Silver Lead	1860	660 Pb ore (29,103 oz Ag)	
	1880	168 Fluorspar	226
Tamar Valley	1870	40 Pb ore (116 oz Ag)	
	1875	20 Pb ore (115 oz Ag)	347
	1875	280 Fluorspar	140
United Tavistock	1855	4¾ Sn ore (?)	300
(Probably Rixhill & Anderton mines)	1860	25½ Sn ore	1,989
Wheal Vincent	1875	3 Sn ore	139
South Ward	1875	22 Pb ore (547 oz Ag)	235
Wheal Zion	1855	271 Cu ore	1,374

S

Tavistock Canal Tonnages

Date	Tonnage	Dues			Dividend		
		£	s	d	£	s	d
To 30 June 1813		638	8	$2\frac{1}{2}$			
June 1814		170	16	$1\frac{1}{2}$			
June 1815		112	18	1			
June 1816		71	11	0			
June 1817		79	5	3			
30 Sept 1818		1,186	2	1			
Dec 1819	21,571	1,032	2	1			
Dec 1820	20,799	1,661	4	$8\frac{1}{2}$	2	0	0
Dec 1821	17,306	1,104	0	0			
Dec 1822	15,024	1,068	0	0	3	0	0
Dec 1823	18,185	1,034	0	0			
Dec 1824	18,626	1,114	0	0			
Dec 1825	18,156	1,095	0	0			
Dec 1826	19,754	1,147	0	0			
Dec 1827	18,233	934	0	0	5	0	0
Dec 1828	15,676	1,297	13	5	2	0	0
Dec 1829	14,146	889	18	$0\frac{1}{2}$	2	11	$4\frac{3}{4}$
Dec 1830	14,371	890	16	$3\frac{1}{2}$	2	0	0
Dec 1831	11,518	679	6	$5\frac{1}{4}$	1	10	0
Dec 1832	14,710	822	16	5	1	10	0
Dec 1833	15,132	740	5	0	1	0	0
Dec 1934	13,756	799	1	0	1	0	0
Dec 1835	15,305	846	11	$1\frac{3}{4}$	1	10	0
Dec 1836	17,516	932	15	$8\frac{1}{4}$	1	10	0
Dec 1837	20,006	1,167	6	8	1	10	0

Date	Tonnage	Dues			Dividend		
		£	s	d	£	s	d
Dec 1838	17,488	1,093	3	2	2	0	0
Dec 1839	19,763	1,074	11	4			
Dec 1840	15,876	1,088	0	0	2	0	0
Dec 1841	16,658	1,105	8	4	2	0	0
Dec 1842	15,735	997	1	3			
Dec 1843	9,978	711	3	3	1	0	0
Dec 1844	13,330	762	14	5			
Dec 1845	14,317	626	8	4			
Dec 1846	14,630	672	14	5			
Dec 1847	20,132	944	11	10	1	0	0
Dec 1848	16,160	768	11	11	1	0	0
Dec 1849	13,221	642	15	2		15	0
Dec 1850	14,020	683	14	2	1	0	0
Dec 1851	14,701	733	13	8	1	0	0
Dec 1852	15,426	750	14	5	1	0	0
Dec 1853	15,639				1	0	0
Dec 1854	15,387					10	0
Dec 1855	18,116				1	0	0
Dec 1856	18,080				1	0	0
Dec 1857	16,791				1	0	0
Dec 1858	16,453	745	4	9	1	0	0
Dec 1859	16,876						
Dec 1860	14,410					10	0
Dec 1861	18,140					10	0
Dec 1862	17,803						
Dec 1863	12,905					7	6
Dec 1864	12,497					5	0
Dec 1865	12,191						
Dec 1866	8,956					2	6
Dec 1867	8,346						
Dec 1868	9,811	239	13	3			

Date	Tonnage	Dues			Dividend		
		£	s	d	£	s	d
Dec 1869	6,369					10	0 out of balance
Dec 1870	783						
Dec 1871	468						
July 1872	309					12	0 final

The dues for 1827 are given only up to 30 Sept.

Note. It would seem that exactly £400 was needed to pay a dividend of £1 a share.

A Recipe for Whitewash

THIS 100-year-old recipe for limewash and whitewash is taken from an account book belonging to the Cotehele Estate, Calstock, now administered by the National Trust. The recipe is still used for mixing lime washes on the estate.

TO MAKE A CHEAP WHITEWASH

1 part salt (Dissolve in hot water)
3 parts lump lime

TO MAKE A GOOD WHITEWASH

Place 1 bushel lump lime into clean tub. Slake it (add water). Cover tub to keep steam in. Strain through fine sieve. Add 3 lb sulphate of zinc, 1 lb alum, 2 lb common salt. Dissolve alum and salt previously in hot water. All whitewash will be improved by adding 2 lb plumber's tallow to each bushel of lime during the boiling process.

If 1 lb of brown sugar is added to each 15 lb of water, it will adhere so firmly on wood and metal that it will be difficult even to scrape off. To prevent lime wash going green, add 1 oz of carbolic acid to each gallon of water.

Index

Illustrations are denoted by bold figures

Rumleigh-brick and arsenic works, 41, 199

St Ann's Chapel, 40, 268
St Dominic, 18, 233–7
St Mellion, 18, 211
St Vincent Mine, 198
Saltash, 17, 27, 35, 211, 213, 217
Sand, 35; as manure, 69–73
Shaft mining—beginnings, 57
Shilla Mill, 22, 208
Shipbuilding, 42
Silver, 13, 21–2, 27, 37; Bere mines, 54–68
Silver Valley Mine, 198
Smelting—Tamar works, 62, 64, 245, 256; Union works, 64, 256
Sortridge Consols, 118, 136
South Tamar Consols, 24, 61, 66–7
Stoke Climsland, 18, 192, 220
Stowford, 24

Tamar Coal, Manure & General Mercantile Co, 180
Tamar Consols Mine—East and South, 54
Tamar, Kit Hill & Callington Railway, 180
Tamar Manure Navigation, 126–8
Tamar Queen, schooner, 43
Tamar, River, 13–14; political boundary, 18, 27; power source, 19; drowned mine, 61; life saving, etc, 84
Tamar Valley—industries, 13; scenery, 15; physical outline, 17; mineral field, 19; mining and effects of, 22; decline, 22

Tanning, 47
Tavistock, 17, 23, 26, 262–3; population trend, 24
Tavy, River, 17, 19, 55, 106, 130, 133, 208
Taylor, John, 64, 103–7; ventilating engine, 110–11; at Wheal Friendship, 130–2
Tin, 21, 28, 35; search at Devon Great Consols Mine, 168, 193, 197; mine outputs, 283–93
Trematon Castle, 72

Venning, James, 182, 218
Victoria, Queen, visit to Endsleigh, 87

Wages, 30, 59, 165
Water-wheels, 19, 31–2, 38–9, 111, 130, 150, **206, 223**
Ward Mine, 65
Watson's Mine, *see* Devon Great Consols Mine
Watson, Peter, 143, 169, 174
Weir Head, 15, 47, 87–8, 90, **260**
Weir Quay, 27, 49, 58, 62, 257
Westlake, Thomas, 41, 244
Wheat prices, 231
Whitleigh, Wheal, 21
Whitsom Mine, 49
William & Mary Mine, 141
Williams, family, 37, 145
Williams Town, 37
Wolfram, 21, 139, 194; outputs, 283–96

Yealm, River, first steamer, 85

Zion, Wheal, 198